CANAL WATER AND WHISKEY
Tall Tales from the Erie Canal Country

CANAL WATER AND WHISKEY

Tall Tales from the Erie Canal Country

by

MARVIN A. RAPP

Fogelsanger Award Recipient for
outstanding contributions to the
Fields of Education and History
—Shippensburg, Pa., 1965

illustrated by

NORMAN TRUESDALE

TWAYNE PUBLISHERS, INC.

NEW YORK 3

CONTENTS

CANAL WATER AND WHISKEY
Tall Tales from the Erie Canal Country

THE AMERICAN TOAST

The Frenchman likes his native wine;
The German likes his beer;
The Englishman likes his 'alf and 'alf
Because it brings him cheer.
The Irishman drinks his whiskey straight
Because it brings him dizziness,
The American has no chance at all,
He drinks the whole damn business.

From Rothman's East Norwich Inn
East Norwich, L. I.
Built in 1732

TO TELL THE TALE

When we arrived at Buffalo,
With Sally, Jack and Hank,
We greased ourselves in tallow fat
And slid off on a plank;
Sally's in the poorhouse,
The rest of the crew's in jail,
And I'm the only ("son——") bugger afloat
That's left to tell the tale.

Sung by Henry "Kip" Conway
Morrisburg, Ontario

Bottoming Out

"BOTTOMING OUT"

Sounds strange, doesn't it? "bottoming out?" For congenial drinkers, it probably should be "bottoms up," "down the hatch," "drain the glasses, boys!" But to all Canawlers (as the Irish called those who worked the Erie Canal) "bottoming out" meant draining Clinton's Ditch—the annual ritual of spring-cleaning the Erie Canal for the start of a new season. Dried to the bottom mud was the accumulated debris dumped into the canal during the year: bottles and jugs, garbage and junk; dead mules and horses, frogs and crayfish, cats and catfish—and bodies, in whole or in part—the unassorted refuse of canal life and death. All fair game for the canal scroungers. What they left behind became the "kitchen middens" of canal archeology—probably the most worthless part of canal remains.

These stories that follow are a kind of "bottoming out" of New York State life along the Erie Canal—a collection of folklore stories, tall tales, anecdotes, newspaper squibs and folk songs; the flotsam and jetsam of the canal era that belonged not to New York State alone but to the whole country, and indeed to the whole world. These tales are probably not the best. The best have probably long since been forgotten—dying with the dead. They are certainly not the worst, for the worst probably couldn't be told. These are the mild "left-overs" that came from Canawlers who were over 90 in my boyhood and whose fathers remembered the early canal. What the real stories must have been will probably never be known. One thing was certain, life was hard on the canal; so was the stuff some of them drank. But there was tradition with it.

Long before the Erie Canal—in the 18th Century days of the French and Indians—even before New York was a State—Lake Champlain, the St. Lawrence River, Lake Ontario, the Niagara River and the upper Great Lakes formed the water lifeline of the fur trade, basic to the economy of America and the world. Its life blood was whiskey, rum and brandy. The spirits flowed abundantly but not freely. As a wag once said, "A belt was worth a pelt." Perhaps this was the way of the wilderness world.

Scientists claim water is older than man and largely responsible for his being; tipplers assert "whiskey is as old as sin and largely responsible for its being." They believed that if water made life possible, whiskey and other spirits made it tolerable. When, in 1825, the Erie Canal joined the lakes and the ocean, the addition of canal water to lake, river, and ocean water created a revolution in the internal commerce of the United States.

These waters met at the Niagara Frontier. So did the men who sailed them. To watermen and their women, these canal waters were their daily bread. To not a few, whiskey was their daily spice; life a day to day combination of both. The water floated their boats; the whiskey their spirits. So from the shores of the canal, and especially from the Niagara country, washed by the water of the river, the lake, and the canal came many of these lusty stories. Probably many of the watermen and their families led ordinary sober, even pious lives, but they never made the stories that were told.

The flavor of most of these stories is Irish. It is a rich flavor, too. A richness that comes from people of deep feeling, of laughter and sadness, of wit and wisdom, of affection and hard work, of religion and politics. Wherever the Irish have gone in the world, the leprechauns, hobgoblins and all their spirits have followed them faithfully. They have touched each spot in the world with the magic of their stories. The Irish are natural storymakers and story tellers.

The joy of my youth was listening to my Irish neighbors spin these tales as I sat near the stoves in their kitchens or on the wharves of the waterfront. In fact, it was not until I was ten that I learned, to my disappointment, that I was not Irish. I had assumed that my name had lost its O' and my church some of its statuary and furniture. I do not think I ever quite forgave my parents for not being Irish. But then in this world you can't have everything.

But I did have a wonderful Grampa. What a man he was! To me, he ran the waterfront. Actually, I guess, he ran the "Buffalo Crick" Railroad. And it kept the waterfront running. I shall never forget the day the Buffalo Crick and the waterfront shut down for 17 minutes, all because of me, age 11, and my Grampa full of years.

I had come down to his shanty and freight office with my father to pick him up at the day's end. As soon as we appeared in the door, things exploded. He shouted orders out the open window behind his back, grabbed several telephones all at once and sent several men in the office flying out of the door with orders. I stood there completely awed, for Grandfather at home was the gentlest of souls. Soon all of the engineers, firemen, brakemen, conductors, dock wallopers, and laborers of the railroad filed into the shanty and freight shed. In strong words, Gramps told them to be quiet, grabbed me under the arms, swung me up on top of the desk and said: "Son, tell them that story you spoke at school."

Grandfather was referring to a homework assignment which called for me to write a story, memorize it and deliver it to the class. As soon as I started to talk, I got over my fright. When I had finished they clapped and yelled "More." So as a last full measure of devotion I threw in the Gettysburg Address. They liked that also. I shall never forget how proud my Gramps was of me that day. My sixth grade was big, very big to him, for he had no education. When I jumped down from the desk, the men crowded about me and started telling me their stories. What stories they were! They told them in rich dialect and expression even taking the parts of the various characters of the story. Perhaps this is the reason why story-telling of this kind has been a hobby and not a vocation with me.

While I continued my education through Colgate and Duke Universities, the waterfront and Canal always drew me back. In my college days I worked on the docks. I wrote my master's and doctorate on the Port of Buffalo. After World War II, on vacations and weekends, over more than a decade, I walked the entire length of the Canal form Buffalo to Albany.

In the middle fifties I took a leave of absence from my teaching duties at the State University College at Buffalo to head the Port Division for the City. Now, like Grampa, I "ran" the waterfront. To meet the challenge of the St. Lawrence Seaway, I helped to develop the Niagara Frontier Port Authority. Later in Albany, as Consultant to the Joint Legislative Committee on the Preservation and Restoration of Historic Sites and the Erie Canal, I sailed the full length of the Canal. Out of that Committee came the recommendation of recreating Canal Town at Fort Hunter.

From all these sources, up and down the Canal, I heard many stories. These are but a few.

When you read these stories, read them aloud—catch the cadence—for they were in the beginning "told" stories not written stories. I never intended to publish them. I wrote them because they were fun and told them because people seemed to enjoy hearing them.

Then one day a great man and a dear friend found out about my stories. His name was Harold Thompson. More than anyone else he is the father of folklore in New York State—author of *Body, Boots and Britches*. At the time he was editor of the New York State Folklore Quarterly. He asked me to send some of these stories to him and I did. Soon I was sending more and more. Most of these have appeared in his and other folklore journals.

For me these stories have been fun. But the most fun

) 14 (

has been working with the truly great story tellers and folk singers of New York State—Carl Carmer, Louis Jones, Frank Warner, Harold Thompson, Walter Edmonds, Moritz Jagendorf, Bill Tyrrell, Dave Ennis, Al Gayer, Ben Botkin, Helen Fraser, Lionel Wyld, Grace Hudowalski, Barbara and Warren Walker, John Sprague, Bill Fenton, Charlie Gosnell, Charlie Snyder, Harvey Chalmers, Jared Van Wagenen, Eric Faigle, Dick Wright, DeWitt Clinton (that's right), Cliff Lord, Margaret Fess, Aggie Underwood, I. Frank Mogavero, Walter Dunn, Les Smith, Walter McCausland, Blake McKelvey, Bob Rose, Bill Cleary, Arnold Barben, Jeanne Schwartz, Ruth Rubin, Millie Taylor, Dan Button, Bob Rayback, Hugh Flick, Jim Frost, Bill Fink, Emily Madden, Eric Brunger, Arch Merrill, Edith Cutting, Harry Douglas, Jeannette Edwards Rattray, Herb Wisbey, and Chuck Wallis—all my waterfront workers and all the Canal Society Canawlers. Special acknowledgment and thanks go to Sam Sesskin. I am also grateful to my good friend Helen A. Fraser, Secretary of the New York Folklore Society and one of the best folklorists in the country, for doing the index. The wonderful illustrations are by Dr. Norman Truesdale, a professor of art (and a damned good one) at the State University College at Buffalo.

To all of them, but most especially to Samuel Hopkins Adams, these stories are dedicated. Sam Adams was a great man and a close friend. He loved the Canal as I do. He served as one of my lecturers at the Canal Seminars, Cooperstown, in the summer of 1957. His book *The Erie Canal* was a joy to children; his *Grandfather Stories* to all, young and old. Sam has gone now but he will never really leave us.

On the last day of the Cooperstown seminars, I wrote some doggerel to Sam Adams which Dave Ennis, Al Gayer and I gave to him. Here it is:

CAPTAIN SAM

Here's a toast to Captain Sam
    Of Adam's basin where bullheads jam;
A boater from the old Canal
    Sam Adams knew its good old Sal.

With pen and ink and paper stock
    He wrote its story, lock by lock;
So none who read would ere forget
    To Erie's water, our endless debt.

We who traveled on this way
    Will n'er forget his wit so gay;
His kindness, patience without end
    Sam Adams—our Canawler friend.

He was pleased, and I was glad. Some time later I asked him if his Grandfather had really told him all of those stories in his book. With a twinkle in his eye, he just smiled and sipped his bourbon—that was a picture that will never fade.

These stories are, of course, not history. They're probably not folklore because I am not exactly sure what folklore is, although there are many who think they know. They're just stories. I hope you enjoy reading them as much as I enjoyed finding them, hearing them and then writing them down. Now read on—and please—aloud.

At Rome a drunken fellow stumbled into the canal. After considerable effort failed to "rake" the body up, some one suggested "trolling" for it with a bottle of whiskey for bait. In a short time the drowned man was drawn up clasping the bottle tightly in his lips. He was "cared for" and will recover, although he had been under water over thirty hours.

Utica Herald, August, 1854, as quoted in "Bottoming Out," official publication of Canal Society of N.Y., #13, 1959, p.7

LIQUOR AND LONGEVITY

The horse and mule live 30 years
And nothing know of wines and beers.
The goat and sheep at 20 die
And never taste of Scotch or Rye.
The cow drinks water by the ton
And at 18 is mostly done.
The dog at 15 cashes in
Without the aid of rum and gin.
The cat in milk and water soaks
And then in 12 short years it croaks.
The modest, sober, bone-dry hen
Lays eggs for nogs, then dies at ten.
All animals are strictly dry:
They sinless live and swiftly die;
But sinful, ginful rum-soaked men
Survive for three score years and ten.
And some of them, a very few,
Stay pickled till they're 92.

UNKNOWN

The Case of the Stiff Canawler

THE CASE OF THE STIFF CANAWLER

Of all of the tales that came out of the western end of the canal, this is perhaps the strangest. It happened at the turn of the century. I first heard it from an eighty-year-old Niagara River man who had the look of the river on his face, a sparkle in his eyes, and a tongue for telling tales. Henry told this story as he relaxed in what must certainly be the last rendezvous of the tow-pathers on the Niagara Frontier: Mutz's Old Saloon[1] on the canal tow path, or what used to be the old canal tow path.

Tug tows and power barges long since have pushed the hustling hoggies with their mules and horses off the canal, tow path and all. The canal itself at Riverside, years ago, took to the Niagara River. At Franz Mutz's Saloon, man has filled the canal bed. Years have erased its markings and the State has taken away its liquor license.

Still the tow path tavern stands, mothering a line of tumbling down fishing shacks, gaily named sporting clubs and just plain cottages on both sides of the saloon along the river bank. The name "tow path" sticks. A fierce pride of oneness with the water marks this colony as a community apart with its own elected mayor. But the tow path is doomed. In another year Thruway bulldozers, making way for the new days, will bury it all in its past.

For now, however, the tavern still stands. Topside it's rainsoaked and sun-baked; below, water-logged and ice-scarred; overall it has a weather-stained gray, matching the foggy overcast that often rides in on the river and seeps into the wood as it does into your bones.

The two-story building leans crazily in all directions as

---

[1] Now, like this story, the tavern belongs to the past.

if it were too tired to hold itself up, and as if it were in a state of momentary hesitation before falling into the river. Attached to the side, a bowling-alley already completely collapsed, seems to be tugging at the rest of the building to join it. In the far corner of what still remains of the alley is a chalk inscription: "Cap Summers rolled three hundred July, 1895."

In its young days, 1892 and immediately thereafter, when the saloon stood erect and fronted proudly on the tow path and a few feet from the canal, many a thirsty driver, as he neared the swinging doors, dropped the reins of his mule team, ran into the tavern, grabbed his schoopper of beer, gulped it down, slapped his money on the bar, dashed out and caught up with his well-trained mules as they continued to walk driverless toward Canal Street and the Buffalo harbor.

When the tow path died with the birth of the Barge Canal, life naturally turned to the river. The backs of the saloon and the canal cottages became more important than the front. Seen from the waterside today it looks as if the river itself had drawn out the backs of the shacks like an accordion and then spread them over the spindles and spiles which stick up out of the river.

As I sat listening to my friend, in the back room of the saloon, I could see the river through the cracks and holes in the floor. Stringy green seaweed clung about the spiles, climbing up and down with the gentle swell of the water. But the river-man was telling his story and my mind went back with him to the old canal days.

When dropping temperature gradually froze the commercial life out of the canal, the canawlers gave up and their kids and other kids took over. With enough water left in the bottom for ice cover, children and adults alike had a ready-made ice rink, 70 feet wide and 365 miles long. Often the boys who lived near the tow path region at Riverside would skate from the old Black Rock Lock past

Mutz's Saloon and onto the double flight at Lockport, miles to the north. On the way back, if the wind was right, they nailed two sticks together like a cross, spread a sheet over them, fastened it tightly, and sailed home on the wind and ice.

South of Mutz's Saloon, where Conjeckety's Creek emptied into the canal behind Squaw Island, was a slack water pool that made a fine ice pond. Today a ship canal lock operated by the Army Engineers, lowers lake and canal boats into the river, or southbound, lifts them up to lake level on their way to the Buffalo harbor and Lake Erie. In 1899, the lock at this point compensated for the same level but the canal stayed inland all the way along the Niagara River. The pond at this point was well protected from the wind so that the ice was unusually smooth for skating.

The winter of 1899 came suddenly with a week of turbulent weather: a severe drop in temperature, a violent sleetstorm, snow, thaw, rain, and again freezing temperatures and snow. Then it cleared and stayed cold. In a few days the boys were skating on the pond. From time beyond their remembering they always sat on one certain spot on the side to put on and take off their skates. This year, to their delight, they discovered near the pond edge an ice hummock, shaped like a chair and just right for changing skates.

That year the young and old alike enjoyed a great season of skating. The ice chair became the gathering point for the gang and the prize to be won in contests. The winner could sit first on the ice throne to take off his skates.

For them, the days lengthened too soon. The sun climbed higher. The canawlers and watermen grew impatient to hit the path. The boys knew their skating days were ending.

Still the ice stayed firm enough on the pond. They kept skating, fearing each day would be the last. Their ice hump melted some and, although still more than man-size, it kept getting smaller. The strange feeling Henry had when he first sat on the ice hump to change his skates seemed to grow stronger. One day, the last it seemed for the year, Henry again sat down on the ice chair. As he finished clamping on his first skate, the strange fear gripped him again, so strongly now that he was not able to put on his other skate. He had a strange feeling, like the feeling one gets on a warm summer evening when a cold blast of air strikes suddenly and dies quickly, or the feeling that sometimes drains strength from legs for no apparent reason. Uncontrollably, Henry turned his head to the back of the ice seat. Terror loosened his face and glazed his eyes. Looking at him out of the ice cake was the face of a man frozen stiff. The chair-like form of the ice hump had followed the sitting contour. Here the canawler had sat down, tired, sick or drunk. Here he had died. The rain and snow had frozen over his body, building up an ice hump that had enveloped him for the whole winter.

As Henry finished his story, he took a long, satisfied draw on his pipe, looked at me for the effect of his story and then added: "Seen many a stiff canawler in my day, but never saw any except old 'ice hump' who didn't ask for another shot to take the cold damp out of his bones. That really would have been 'whiskey on the rocks!' "

IRISH DIGGERS AND WHISKEY JIGGERS

For the most part, the Irish bogtrotters dug the Erie Canal. For their ditch-digging chores they received ten dollars a month and board plus a number of jiggers of whiskey. The jigger was a small measure about one-third the size of an ordinary tumbler. When inquiring of a foreman for work, a laborer never asked, "What wages do you pay?" He simply asked, "How many jiggers do ye give?"

Public Service of State of New York
Vol. 1 Jones Osgood and Co., 455-56

COME, COME AWAY, HO

Come, come away, ho,
To the barroom go,
Play a little at high-10
Take a drink at every throw
For sure to Heaven you will go.
Come, ho, jolly foe.
Why delay you to go.

So down the seller will pour it;
Though it grieve him sore
For, loss of pence full well he knows,
Will grieve him much more.

Canawl Water and Whiskey

CANAWL WATER AND WHISKEY

It was 1825. The canal was coming. Along the right of way from the Hudson River to Lake Erie, hopes were high and real estate values were going higher. Yankees and Yorkers, sharp for a bargain, counted their future blessings in the currency of the day: coonskins, produce and Spanish quarters. To the pot-stove philosophers of the small wilderness settlement of Buffalo, the canal and little else mattered. Soon the guess-and-gamble travel over the rutted Genesee Road and the portage-broken Ontario-Niagara waterway would give way to the smooth green waters of the Grand Canal.

Buried in the newspaper files and in some memories, were the unpleasant recollections of the burning of Buffalo during the War of 1812 and the death struggle with Black Rock over the western terminus of the canal. All that was yesterday. The future belonged to the little village perched atop a low bluff overlooking Buffalo Creek and "Erie's Waters." The dreamers let their imaginations follow their gaze out over the harbor and across the lake to the distant horizon. They dotted the "sweet waters" with the sails of hundreds of vessels and counted the freight from the far and still unpeopled West. These Buffalo pioneers had a right to dream. It was 1825. The canal was coming. So were the Irish.

With pick and shovel and bone-muscle born of the peat bogs and green sod of the counties of Cork and Clare, the Irish inched their way through the rich York soil. Across fields and creeks, through swamps, sand and rock, they moved the canal westward. Little wonder the hard-working, hard-living Irish claimed that they had clawed out the canal with their bare fingers and then filled it with their honest sweat. They were proud of their canawl, as they called it, and prouder still of the name, canawler. Those who shouted, "Folly, Clinton's folly!" were answered by digging. To those who laughed and said that neither Governor DeWitt Clinton nor the Irish could make water run uphill, they replied by building the locks. The canal was coming. The Irish would see to that.

Soon the Tonawanda-Buffalo leg was under construction. A part of a day's travel would take the people to the diggings where Irish chanteys filled the Niagara air with an Erin brogue. After days which must have seemed years to those who waited in Buffalo, the ditch left the river's edge and headed straight inland for the Little Buffalo Creek, which emptied into the harbor. In a future day, that last section would become a part of the Niagara section of the Governor Dewey Thruway. But now its future as canal lay ahead.

Villagers gathered to watch the canawlers lean-to on their picks against the sandy loam. Whatever official celebration might follow the formal completion of the work, they meant to witness the real finish. With the goal so close at hand, the diggers lost no time. For the impatient pioneers, however, the work moved much too slowly. They watched and waited anxiously. Finally, to someone with American frontier resourcefulness a "Yankee" idea occurred —or so legend has it.

The next morning, when the Irish took their places in the ditch, they noticed barrels carefully placed at measured intervals along the route of the canal. They were not ordinary barrels, but whiskey barrels. What was more, they were full. The game was soon out. As the Irish dug their way to a barrel, they drained it and moved on to the next and the next until they reached the Little Buffalo Creek. Old timers had no trouble boasting that this was the fastest diggin' and drinkin' the canawl had ever seen.

For the people of Buffalo the waiting was over. The canal, *their* canal, had come. Tomorrow was here. When the formal completion was celebrated, Governor Clinton, from aboard the canal boat "Seneca Chief," dumped a cask of pure Lake Erie water into the briny waters of the Atlantic Ocean. The official state representatives and other dignitaries toasted the "wedding of the waters" with imported champagne. At least the pioneers on the western frontier heard it rumored that way. It was all right, they thought, for the civilized dandies of the East to toast their canal with imported champagne if they wanted to. But for them, for those who did the diggin', no one would ever make them believe that on that occasion champagne was as fittin' as canawl water with a whiskey chaser.

DIG A COMPLETE CANAL

I've always liked the logic used by a member of the Legislature at the time it was debating to dig a complete canal or just segments.

"Might just as well dig a complete canal—same way if you're going to get married. You might just as well marry a pretty girl as an ugly one, especially if you're going to be home much."

Old Beales and Coffee Beans

OLD BEALES AND COFFEE BEANS

Buffalo—October 17, 1844

Old Beales relaxed contentedly on a hogshead barrel which was nudged snugly against a wooden fence. He was whittlin' away. As his eyes took in the little waterfront development in front of him, a smile creased his face. "T'ain't giv'n to many," Beales mumbled to himself, "to found a settlement. But this'n's mine and I christened it with my name. Got it right on the sternboard. Bealesville's sure's better'n Sandy Town for a name. Sumpin' a man kin be proud of. Diff'runt from a year ago when I first stranded on these shores. 'Twarn't worth a second look-see. Now take a readin'. Not bad a'tall for an old water-rat the likes of me. Not bad a'tall."

"If that ole patched-up canawler of mine hadn't busted its rotten seams that night, I might still of been poundin' the towpath from Ithacy to Buffalo. Come to think of it, it's downright funny. The Ole Erie ditch took one beat up barge 'way from me, and Lake Erie washed up a dozen to take its place. That's a pretty good deal even for an 'Ole watchstuffer' like me. Lucky I sold my cargo the night before. That sure helped launch my land-sailing venture here."

As Beales savored this thought for all the goodness in it, a voice broke his pleasant reverie.

"What ya dreamin' up Beales? Another 'black-leg' deal?"

"Oh, it's you Jake," said Beales as he turned around, "what's eatin' your rotten insides?"

"Nothin'. Loadin's slow on the dock this mornin', so I thought I'd come over and see who you was fixin' to skin today."

"You, of course, you leather-hided son-of-a-mule," Beales yelled and laughed at the same time.

"My hide wouldn't be worth much," Jake countered, "it's pretty well worn." As he said this, Jake held up his hands. They were the hands of a real water-rat. The mark of the rope could be plainly seen across the palm. Jake belonged. He was part water, part sand, part wind; he was all canawler.

"Jake, I was just 'memberin' a year ago."

" 'Twas just about a year ago your ole canal tub went awash at the Rock, if I 'member rightly," Jake said. "You know Beales, it always seemed a queer bit funny to me that you got rid of your load 'fore she went down. Seems I recall you had the bottom insured but not the cargo."

"Seems I 'member sumpin' like that," Beales said knowingly. "But Jake, 'taint always healthy to have too good a memory here on the Buffalo water-front. But that makes no never mind Jake. You have to give that these were mighty poor washings before I got here."

"Got to say aye aye to that, Beales. This sandy stretch fore and aft 'twarn't nothin' but a barge graveyard 'fore you took hold."

Beales was thinking. More to himself than to Jake he mumbled, "Yeah, sure was diff'runt a year ago."

Jake and Beales were right. Things had certainly changed in Sandy Town since Beales took over. That morning about a year ago when his boat went down at Black Rock a few miles to the north on the Niagara River, Beales' stock went up. It seemed as if that morning were only yesterday. By the time he reached the Rock his feet were sore. He had spelled off the skinners on the towpath all the way from Ithaca. As Captain of his barge, he was unused to walking the mules because most of his sailing days had been spent at the tiller. That's where he was when the water started gushing in the hold that morning a year ago. At sight of the water, he jumped ashore and watched the barge settle to the bottom. As he stared at the barge sitting dumb-like on the bottom of the canal, he decided that he had all he wanted of the canawler's life. While he dangled his tired feet in the cool water, he watched and thought and planned. Although it was early in the morning, the bargers had already begun to move toward Commercial Slip several miles south of Black Rock in the Buffalo harbor.

What a sight this canal procession made as the barge mules straining against their sweat-soaked leather traces dragged their west-bound cargo along the last stretch of canal. The mules kicked up puffs of brownish dust as their hoofs bit into the towpath and the skinners fore and aft caught up the slow loping rhythm of the mules in a song of the canal. Alongside the towpath, on the right, the Niagara River plunged swiftly towards the Falls some twenty miles to the north. The French had called these rapids opposite what one day would be Buffalo, Le Petite Rapids, the Little Rapids. On the left side of the towpath, the canal, soft and still by contrast, came to life as the broad blunt bows of the barges rolled up continuous waves which slapped noisily against the towpath. From the other side of the canal, almost in simple counterpoint, came the quiet sound of the same waves as they dwindled into ripples and broke like muffled echoes against the towpath.

When the river water had drawn some of the fire out of his feet, Beales slipped on his faded socks, covered them with what were once shoes, and scrambled up the bank. At the top, he sucked in some fresh Niagara air, braced his shoulders, faced southward and headed down the path toward Buffalo. As he walked, he wondered where the thousands of immigrants had come from and where they were going. It seemed to him that most of Europe and all of the east coast were walking or riding westward on and along the Erie Canal. He wondered how long the immigrants entering Buffalo that morning would have to wait before they could book passage to the West. He knew that crowded conditions aboard the immigrant vessels sometimes made it necessary for families to wait weeks before they were able to embark. In fact, he had seen many families, unable to book passage or find lodging for the night, sleeping atop their baggage along the wharves. Those with some money took rooms in the cheap hotels which dotted the waterfront, and more often than not, they lost all of their money and were fortunate to get away with their lives.

By the time Beales had reached the outskirts of Buffalo, the morning was well advanced. Some distance from Commercial Slip the space between the canal and lake widened. Old Beales noticed that this section of land had changed to a sandy loam. As he scanned the area, an object over to his right caught his eye. It was along the water's edge of the lake. He had heard this region called Sandy Town but he had never examined it closely. He decided now was the time.

As he approached the lake, he was soon able to identify the objects that dotted the shore. Decaying barges and small lake vessels abandoned by their masters had been driven deeply into the soft sand by the pounding lake waves. Their ribs bleached white by the sun and sand lay exposed like the skeletons of some prehistoric beasts. Traces of once gaudy paint now streaked, blistered, peeled, made hollow mockery of their former fame and fortune. Even now the faded name printed impressively on the tail board seemed more like a grave marker.

Beales surveyed the barges with the practiced eye of a canawler. Some were old friends. Many brought back to his mind wonderful tales of the raging canal. Perhaps his "Betsy" would soon join this graveyard of forgotten canawlers. Spotting one barge less old than the others which had just recently been condemned to dry land sailing, Beales decided to explore. He shinnied up the side. On deck, he almost instinctively headed for the Captain's quarters. No more than a gentle push forced the rusted lock catch. Beales found himself inside. As soon as he closed the door, the dust began to settle back to its accustomed spots about the room and the cobwebs relaxed. A water-rat, four-legged variety, disturbed in its meal of fresh fish, disappeared quickly into its hole. "That's one rat," said Beales aloud to himself, "who didn't desert the sinking ship." Along the portside of the room, Beales spotted a couch which the rats had used as a source of straw for their nest building. While dampness and age had dulled the luster of its appointments and rotted its panelling, the quarters gave evidence of having been ship-shape the day the barge was abandoned. Beales wondered who the Captain had been. Why had she been abandoned? As these thoughts crossed his mind, he sat down in what had been the Captain's leather chair. He felt at home. As his eye appraised the room, he knew she had been a better tub than Betsy.

He looked aft through the tiny window toward the Grand Canal. An endless parade of canal boats stretched from the Rock to Buffalo. Atop the barges were men and women of all types. Some richly, some poorly dressed. Some with the costumes of Switzerland and Germany; others with those of the Scandinavian countries. Europe was on the march. Once again as Beales mused, he wondered where they were all going; what part of the West they would make their home in. Perhaps it would be Illinois, Ohio, Michigan or the wild land beyond. He wondered, too, where they would stay that night in Buffalo. Probably the rich could easily get accommodations at the Mansion House. The poor, but not destitute class, might find cover in some of the waterfront dives. The completely unblessed, however, would undoubtedly sleep atop the cargo tarpaulins on the wharves. Then a thought struck Beales. Like all good ideas, it came swift and sure. "A little fixin' might turn some of these barges into liveable houses. After all a canal barge was a sort of floating house anyhow. Conversion would be easy." For a quiet while, Beales thought hard on this idea. Then he stood up and opened the door. The lake breeze flurried the room a bit as he stepped out of the cabin. He closed the door, shinnied down the side of the barge and walked between the barges scattered hither and yon along the beach. When he reached the shore he stood a moment watching the rhythmic swells of the lake break into gentle rolls and disappear into the high sands as they reached themselves thin. Still lost in thought, he leaned over, cupped his hand, and drank the cool lake water. It tasted good and felt good as he threw some of it in his face.

As he stood up, still shaking his face, he noticed someone sitting on the shore bank whittling. Beales walked toward the figure slowly. When he was within voice distance, he called out, "Top o' mornin' to ya."

The man raised his head, looked toward the voice, studied the approaching figure for a moment, and said noncommittally, "Mornin'."

"You from here-abouts?" Beales asked.

"Yeah you could say that," the whittler answered.

"Live here?" Beales said.

"Sorta," came the answer.

"What do ya mean 'sorta'?"

"Well," said the whittler, "I live a little here and a little there." Then after a very significant pause, he looked straight into Beales' eyes and said, "You're a mighty nosey stranger. What's really eatin' away at you?"

Beales had to smile at the whittler's mind reading. "I'm a canawler. Name's Beales. Who are you?"

"'Taint none of your damn business, but the name's Jake and I am and have been a canawler, scooper, carter— hell! I'm a water-rat. Been one since I was knee-high to a whiffle tree."

Beales chuckled at this. It took no mind reading to

FRP creates successful connections between organizations and individuals through custom books.

 Favorite Recipes® Press

Favorite Recipes Press, an imprint of FRP, Inc., located in Nashville, Tennessee, is one of the nation's best-known and most-respected cookbook companies. Favorite Recipes Press began by publishing cookbooks for its parent company, Southwestern/Great American, in 1961. FRP, Inc., is now a wholly owned subsidiary of the Southwestern/Great American family of companies, and under the Favorite Recipes Press imprint has produced hundreds of custom cookbook titles for nonprofit organizations, companies, and individuals.

Other FRP, Inc., imprints include

Additional titles published by FRP, Inc., are

Favorite Recipes of Home Economics Teachers

Cooking Up a Classic Christmas	Recipes Worth Sharing	More Recipes Worth Sharing	The Hunter's Table	The Vintner's Table

Junior Leagues In the Kitchen with Kids: Everyday Recipes & Activities for Healthy Living

Almost Homemade

The Illustrated Encyclopedia of American Cooking

Classic
JUNIOR LEAGUE®
COOKBOOK COLLECTION

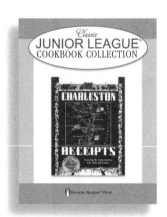

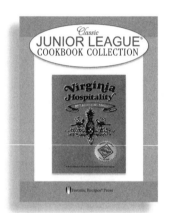

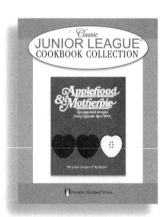

This collection includes six of the most well known and respected Junior League cookbooks of all time; combined there are more than 2,000 pages with 4,000 regionally inspired, tried-and-true recipes. Collectively, over 2,000,000 copies of these cookbooks have sold over a span of 60 years.

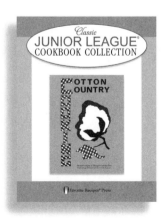

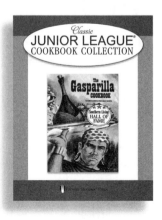

some of these barges into liveable houses. After all a canal barge was a sort of floating house anyhow. Conversion would be easy." For a quiet while, Beales thought hard on this idea. Then he stood up and opened the door. The lake breeze flurried the room a bit as he stepped out of the cabin. He closed the door, shinnied down the side of the barge and walked between the barges scattered hither and yon along the beach. When he reached the shore he stood a moment watching the rhythmic swells of the lake break into gentle rolls and disappear into the high sands as they reached themselves thin. Still lost in thought, he leaned over, cupped his hand, and drank the cool lake water. It tasted good and felt good as he threw some of it in his face.

As he stood up, still shaking his face, he noticed someone sitting on the shore bank whittling. Beales walked toward the figure slowly. When he was within voice distance, he called out, "Top o' mornin' to ya."

The man raised his head, looked toward the voice, studied the approaching figure for a moment, and said noncommittally, "Mornin'."

"You from here-abouts?" Beales asked.

"Yeah you could say that," the whittler answered.

"Live here?" Beales said.

"Sorta," came the answer.

"What do ya mean 'sorta'?"

"Well," said the whittler, "I live a little here and a little there." Then after a very significant pause, he looked straight into Beales' eyes and said, "You're a mighty nosey stranger. What's really eatin' away at you?"

Beales had to smile at the whittler's mind reading. "I'm a canawler. Name's Beales. Who are you?"

"'Taint none of your damn business, but the name's Jake and I am and have been a canawler, scooper, carter—hell! I'm a water-rat. Been one since I was knee-high to a whiffle tree."

Beales chuckled at this. It took no mind reading to

watched the barge settle to the bottom. As he stared at the barge sitting dumb-like on the bottom of the canal, he decided that he had all he wanted of the canawler's life. While he dangled his tired feet in the cool water, he watched and thought and planned. Although it was early in the morning, the bargers had already begun to move toward Commercial Slip several miles south of Black Rock in the Buffalo harbor.

What a sight this canal procession made as the barge mules straining against their sweat-soaked leather traces dragged their west-bound cargo along the last stretch of canal. The mules kicked up puffs of brownish dust as their hoofs bit into the towpath and the skinners fore and aft caught up the slow loping rhythm of the mules in a song of the canal. Alongside the towpath, on the right, the Niagara River plunged swiftly towards the Falls some twenty miles to the north. The French had called these rapids opposite what one day would be Buffalo, Le Petite Rapids, the Little Rapids. On the left side of the towpath, the canal, soft and still by contrast, came to life as the broad blunt bows of the barges rolled up continuous waves which slapped noisily against the towpath. From the other side of the canal, almost in simple counterpoint, came the quiet sound of the same waves as they dwindled into ripples and broke like muffled echoes against the towpath.

When the river water had drawn some of the fire out of his feet, Beales slipped on his faded socks, covered them with what were once shoes, and scrambled up the bank. At the top, he sucked in some fresh Niagara air, braced his shoulders, faced southward and headed down the path toward Buffalo. As he walked, he wondered where the thousands of immigrants had come from and where they were going. It seemed to him that most of Europe and all of the east coast were walking or riding westward on and along the Erie Canal. He wondered how long the immigrants entering Buffalo that morning would have to wait before they could book passage to the West. He knew that crowded conditions aboard the immigrant vessels sometimes made it necessary for families to wait weeks before they were able to embark. In fact, he had seen many families, unable to book passage or find lodging for the night, sleeping atop their baggage along the wharves. Those with some money took rooms in the cheap hotels which dotted the waterfront, and more often than not, they lost all of their money and were fortunate to get away with their lives.

By the time Beales had reached the outskirts of Buffalo, the morning was well advanced. Some distance from Commercial Slip the space between the canal and lake widened. Old Beales noticed that this section of land had changed to a sandy loam. As he scanned the area, an object over to his right caught his eye. It was along the water's edge of the lake. He had heard this region called Sandy Town but he had never examined it closely. He decided now was the time.

As he approached the lake, he was soon able to identify the objects that dotted the shore. Decaying barges and small lake vessels abandoned by their masters had been driven deeply into the soft sand by the pounding lake waves. Their ribs bleached white by the sun and sand lay exposed like the skeletons of some prehistoric beasts. Traces of once gaudy paint now streaked, blistered, peeled, made hollow mockery of their former fame and fortune. Even now the faded name printed impressively on the tail board seemed more like a grave marker.

Beales surveyed the barges with the practiced eye of a canawler. Some were old friends. Many brought back to his mind wonderful tales of the raging canal. Perhaps his "Betsy" would soon join this graveyard of forgotten canawlers. Spotting one barge less old than the others which had just recently been condemned to dry land sailing, Beales decided to explore. He shinnied up the side. On

deck, he almost instinctively headed for the Captain's quarters. No more than a gentle push forced the rusted lock catch. Beales found himself inside. As soon as he closed the door, the dust began to settle back to its accustomed spots about the room and the cobwebs relaxed. A water-rat, four-legged variety, disturbed in its meal of fresh fish, disappeared quickly into its hole. "That's one rat," said Beales aloud to himself, "who didn't desert the sinking ship." Along the portside of the room, Beales spotted a couch which the rats had used as a source of straw for their nest building. While dampness and age had dulled the luster of its appointments and rotted its panelling, the quarters gave evidence of having been ship-shape the day the barge was abandoned. Beales wondered who the Captain had been. Why had she been abandoned? As these thoughts crossed his mind, he sat down in what had been the Captain's leather chair. He felt at home. As his eye appraised the room, he knew she had been a better tub than Betsy.

He looked aft through the tiny window toward the Grand Canal. An endless parade of canal boats stretched from the Rock to Buffalo. Atop the barges were men and women of all types. Some richly, some poorly dressed. Some with the costumes of Switzerland and Germany; others with those of the Scandinavian countries. Europe was on the march. Once again as Beales mused, he wondered where they were all going; what part of the West they would make their home in. Perhaps it would be Illinois, Ohio, Michigan or the wild land beyond. He wondered, too, where they would stay that night in Buffalo. Probably the rich could easily get accommodations at the Mansion House. The poor, but not destitute class, might find comfort in some of the waterfront dives. The completely unblessed, however, would undoubtedly sleep atop the cargo tarpaulins on the wharves. Then a thought struck Beales. Like all good ideas, it came swift and sure. "A little fixin' might know Jake spoke the truth. He looked the part. "Who owns this land?" inquired Beales.

"Guess I do," came the unexpected answer.

"You do?" exclaimed Beales.

"Yeah, I guess I do, and if you are a Yorker, it be part yourn' too. This is squatter land—the York State milestrip. And them's abandoned barges over there belongin' to no one."

The thought Beales had been mulling over in his mind ever since leaving the barge awakened once more and began to take shape. With pioneers moving westward by the thousand, here was an excellent place less than a quarter of a mile from Commercial Slip for the poor and almost destitute pioneers to lay over while awaiting passage to the West on the crowded lake steamers. Beales looked squarely at Jake and said, "Ever handle a hammer?"

"Damn you stranger," said Jake, "ain't never seen or heard of a canawler who couldn't handle a hammer better'n some who call themselves carpenters."

Beales knew this to be true, but it was just a way of opening the conversation on the point he wished to discuss. "How'd you like to work for me?" Beales offered.

"Look here stranger," said Jake, "I don't know you beyond you sayin' your name's Beales. But 'bout far as I'm concerned you're nothin' but a canawl rat and that is just a mite bit lower than a water-rat. It's probably been so long since you had your paws on a Spanish two-bit piece you wouldn't know what they are. So let's stow the gab."

Beales reached into his pocket and pulled out a bag containing the hard money he had received for the sale of his cargo. He opened the bag and Jake peeked in. Jake gave a low hissing sound that would have been a whistle if he had had teeth instead of their rotting stumps. "Stranger, you've got yourself a man. Let's get at it."

That had been the start of Bealesville. Jake had been in at the birth pains. Taking the best barges first, Jake and

Old Beales repaired them very quickly. From the beginning, the venture had been a success. No sooner had the first been completed, than it was rented immediately by a family heading west. The renter, however, secured employment in one of the commission houses the very day he arrived and so never moved on. Beales had himself a permanent tenant.

One by one the barges were completed. None was ever vacant a day. When the barges on shore had been converted, Beales went out and salvaged others and dragged them up onto his sandy land. The little squatter colony grew rapidly. In a very short time, people began to refer to it as Bealesville. This was a significant tribute to Old Beales, who by now, had become the power behind squatter sovereignty in Buffalo.

Beales began to smile as these thoughts crossed his mind. He had been so lost in recalling the past year, that he had forgotten that Jake was standing next to him. He did not realize how long he had been silent until he looked down at the pile of shavings at his feet, then he knew that it must have been some time. Looking over at Jake, who by now was also whittling, Beales said apologetically, "Sorry Jake, I was just a-thinkin'."

" 'Bout what?" said Jake.

" 'Bout the difference."

"So was I," said Jake. "Say, 'member that old stew bum what tried to beat you out of a week's rent? I think if I hadn't come in at the right moment, you'd a'beat his brains out with that water-logged club you had."

"Think I would have," said Beales. "That dirty piece of seaweed was three parts black strap and one part human. All he ever did was suck it up and spew it out. Only man I knew with a continuous two-way gut. I sure thought he had put the bite on me that time."

"What gets me, Beales," said Jake, "is how you ever came to believe in him. All's I was interested in was keeping you from bashing his head in. I didn't believe him when he said he know'd how to bring back the face on a smooth Spanish two-bitter."

"Jake, I reckon I dunno why I let him go in return for that witch's brew he scribbled out for me. But I guess it's 'cause I had beat him so close to the edge of his life that I didn't think he had any more lie in him."

"'Member the night we mixed that God-awful stuff, Beales? Sure stunk up the barge. Then we took the quarters, dipped them in the brew for a few minutes and pulled 'em out. Beales, you know that drunk must have been somebody once 'cause his brew sure worked. I'll never forget your puss when you saw the image come back on that smooth two-bitter. I think you bought every worn Spanish piece on the waterfront that next week for fifteen cents each. And then dipped 'em and peddled 'em for their face value at twenty-five cents. You ole skinflint, when you gonna tell me how you do it?"

"Jake, you nor anybody else is ever gonna get that brew formula outa me. So far as I know, that stew-bum and I are the only ones who know and I don't guess he'll ever stick his bow in here again."

"Do you still have the water-rats bringing in smooth pieces, Beales?"

"I sure do, Jake, and believe me, business has been mighty good these last six months. You know my Spanish exchange and my rents sure helped to launch my cargo scroungin'. Ya know Jake, I've had plenty of good luck with scroungin'. 'Member the time the propeller *Princeton* got itself stormbound off Fair Port? It was hot and muggy and she had a load of 250 dressed hogs. What a load that was. What was it that eastern dandy said, when the *Princeton* pulled into Buffalo creek? 'Captain, your meat has acquired a greenish hue and oriental fragrance.' Don't know what he meant by all those big words Jake, but he was sure half right. The hogs was sure green. Jake, do ya ever expect to smell anything that stunk like those hogs? It was worse than the stew's brew."

"Stinkers is right," said Jake, "but as I recall, they brought you a hundred dollars profit at the local lard oil refiners. Not bad dealing for a half hour of dickerin'."

Jake and Beales looked at each other and burst out in belly guffaws that almost rocked them off their barrels.

"But the best damn load I ever scrounged, Jake, was them coffee beans. Do ya 'member? The boat went down over yonder just off the light."

"Yeah," said Jake, "and if I remember my log rightly, you was over there 'fore her belly hit the bottom. And by the time she was scrapin' the bottom, you had yourself a deal. Never did know how you souped them up, but I sure can remember you spreadin' 'em out right over there on the sand."

"Jake, I dried 'em, roasted 'em, and ground 'em. 'Member the white packages we put them in? I can still see the pretty letterin'. *Buffalo's Pure Ground Coffee*. Jake, did you know I made the best haul of my life with those coffee beans in Cleveland? Sold the whole cargo for 100% profit. A real black leg haul. From then on, the canawlers tagged me "Old Beales and Coffee Beans." You know Jake, those dirty sons of whiffle trees still yell that at me as they float past.

"But here's my pride, Jake," Beales said, as he patted the fence against which he was leaning. This high board fence enclosed an area just off Washington Street near the Canal. Within the enclosure, Beales stored old doors, sash, blinds, mantles, ship chandlery, figurines, in fact the interior of the warehouse within the fenced area looked very much like a museum of waterfront abracadabra. Here he had gathered, dried and sold the flotsam and jetsam of Lake Erie and the Erie Canal. He furnished his house boats and converted barges with this second-hand furniture.

While Beales patted the fence affectionately, another thought entered his mind. It was a black thought and he always tried to push it aside. But it always kept coming back. With a serious, almost frightened expression on his face, Beales turned slowly to Jake and said, "Jake, ya know, when I see those black devil clouds gatherin' out there over the lake at sundown as they are right now, I get sceered of them waters."

"Why Beales, you ole son of a shady bargain, I never heard tell of you being sceered of anything or anybody."

"You're right Jake. As far as ornery humans is concerned, I always figured I could hold my own against canawler or sailor, fresh or salt. Never feared squatters, floaters, watch stuffers, black legs, migrants, not by a dum sight. Fact is, never feared anything that talked. I understand talk. It's the dumb things I'm scared of. Take that lake yonder. I'm scared to death of Erie when she scowls nasty like she's doin' now."

"Beales I always thought if any son of a whiffle tree or mast knowed these waters, it was you. Why the canawlers and fresh water boys think you can talk with the waters. Some say they see you."

"Well if they see me on the shore talking, it was to myself, 'cause those dumb waters ain't talked to me or anybody else."

"Beales, I dunno what you're babblin' about. You know damn well Erie's given you all you got. Fetched it up and dumped it in your front yard."

"You're right, Jake," Beales agreed. "These waters have been mighty sweet to my taste. Jake, did you know that the red devils used to call Erie 'The Sweet Waters'? Yeah, I suppose you can say the water's been good to me. But Jake, you know things that talk, give, but by gad they 'spect to get in return. I understand that. But these waters don't talk, Jake. If they give, when are they gonna come to get? Jake, some day they're gonna come and get me and all I got. They plumb scare me. They're dumb things, Jake. I don't know them."

Newspaper article, Buffalo *Commercial Advertiser*, October 18, 1844.
"The hurricane storm that swept tidal waves all the way up to Seneca Street causing great property damage, completely wiped out Bealesville."

For old Beales, the sweet water had left a bitter taste.

LET THE STORM COME DOWN

The sun is no longer in view,
The clouds have begun to frown,
But, with a bumper or two,
We'll say, let the storm come down.
And the song we'll sing, one and all,
While the storm around us pelts,
A life on the muddy canawl,
Oh, we don't want nothin' else.

From *Body, Boots and Britches*
By Harold W. Thompson
Page 254

WHISKEY CARGO AND JOHN WILKES BOOTH

To most any Chicago barkeep at the turn of the century, a call for a shot of Mary Smith meant the best whiskey in the house. It marked the buyer a judge of good liquor and the bartender an expert in whiskey folklore—that is, if he knew the whole story behind the name of the whiskey. Few did.

Those who did know always told the story. It went with the drink like a chaser. It was quite a tale—this story of the *Mary Smith* and her cargo. It all began (the man behind the bar would usually say) one stormy night on Lake Erie—April 17, 1859, to be exact. The schooner *Mary Smith*, out of Chicago, ran into bad weather and heavy seas not too far west of its Buffalo destination. With the good and experienced hands she had before the mast and tiller, the schooner should have ridden out the storm. Strangely enough, she didn't. Only the mate and two hands managed to escape in a small boat before the schooner sank in deep water twenty miles from Buffalo a little before daybreak. Save for these three, all hands were lost along with forty-thousand gallons of the choicest spirits from mid-western distilleries. This wet cargo on the bottom of Lake Erie was, of course, the point of the story.

The whiskey remained in the hold of the *Mary Smith* for 14 years undisturbed—at least undisturbed by humans. The deep water discouraged salvage attempts. As the years rolled on, the story of the *Mary Smith* grew. As her whiskey cargo aged, the price increased accordingly. What could be better, thought many a tippler, as he wetted his lips with a whiskey bearing the name Mary Smith, than a taste of the real Mary Smith aged in oaken barrels for 14 years and cooled all that time by the bottom waters of Lake Erie. It was enough to make some men want to go diving for it. None did, however. They just talked about it. Occasionally they lifted their glasses in a toast to the cargo of the *Mary Smith*—"May her barrel seams stay tight and her whiskey never be watered."

The men, however, who sell whiskey and drink whiskey have long memories for their favorite liquor. Now and again those with the longest memories and keenest taste for both spirits and money would speculate on the constantly increasing value of the whiskey cargo. One such man lived in Chicago in those years. His name was Ralph Bayne. Though he had accomplished little else, he had, at an early age, acquired a goodly inheritance from his family and an exacting taste for fine liquor.

Across famous bars in Chicago, he had heard with many a drink the story of the lost cargo of the schooner *Mary Smith*. Being an adventuresome sort of fellow, he inquired about the location of the wreck and the possibility of the raising of the cargo. He found out exactly where it was and how it could be raised. From a Chicago firm he negotiated a contract that would pay him $20 a gallon for all the *Mary Smith* liquor he delivered. With this contract, a good crew, and a lively retinue, Bayne sailed out of the Chicago river April 17, 1873, 14 years to the day that the *Mary Smith* met her fate.

Bayne brought with him aboard the sloop a father and son team of divers named Falcon. In those days, Chicago marine interests considered these two the best divers around the city. To take care of his legal and business interests, Bayne engaged a lawyer named Luther Laflin Mills. For just plain fun around the poker table, Bayne invited a whiskey-drinking friend. History and the story leave him nameless.

The trip proved uneventful. They played poker, drank, and sang. In idle moments, Bayne multiplied 40,000 gallons by $20 per gallon. The result always came out the same, $800,000. The thought of the money warmed the cockles of his wallet; the thought of the whiskey whetted his taste buds. He found both thoughts pleasant. Finally, on a still, warm day the sloop dropped anchor at what had become the hallowed spot of some whiskey drinkers, the place where the *Mary Smith* sank. The elder Falcon wasted no time in donning his diving suit. His son manned the air line. Being French, the Falcons were understandably demon-strative. The father loved the boy very deeply. Not knowing the water's depth, or the full risk involved, just before he stepped over the side he grabbed his son impulsively, pressed him close against his chest in a warm embrace, then pushed him out at arms length, looked at him tenderly for a moment and then kissed him quickly and softly on both cheeks.

Watching this touching scene from the taffrail, Bayne's poker-playing friend, filled with plenty of whiskey, removed his hat, clutched a rope with his left hand, extended his right hand, palm up, struck a dramatic pose, and declaimed,

Oh! Give him a sepulchre broad as the sweep
Of the tidal wave's measureless motion;
Lay our hero to sleep in the arms of the deep
Since his life was as free as the ocean.

The quiet waters seemed to magnify his voice. It made majestic what he had meant to be mockery.

Falcon was already disappearing below the surface as the words floated over the water. Part way down a kink developed in the air line. Desperately the elder Falcon tried to get it out. On the bottom he signalled for slack in the line hoping this would clear it. It failed. With his air supply cut off, his moments were now numbered. He began to grow faint. Still he struggled to straighten the line, but to no avail. Just before he blacked out he frantically pulled the air line three times, the danger signal. Young Falcon and the crew worked fast. They pulled him up as quickly as possible. When they stripped off his helmet the old man was already unconscious and almost lifeless. They applied artificial respiration immediately and in time the old man came around. Understandably he would have no more diving for that day or that trip. So, reluctantly Bayne weighed anchor and returned to Chicago. Since that unsuccessful attempt, there is no record of anyone trying to reach the cargo of the *Mary Smith*. For all anyone knows, she is still there with 40,000 gallons of aged whiskey which may or may not be watered. Old-timers among Buffalo mariners, however, do not recall her name or story. Newspapers of her time carry no reference to her and histories of the Great Lakes list no schooner of that name. Yet the story by a Chicago correspondent of the New York *Sun* appeared in the Buffalo *Enquirer*, May 24, 1898.

Ordinarily, this would have ended the story if it had not been for something said the day of the unsuccessful dive. Luther Mills, the lawyer on the trip who later attained great stature in that profession in Chicago, had been struck by the beauty of the words spoken by the friend at the taffrail as Falcon disappeared into the water. Anxious to learn the whole poem and the name of the author, Mills, some years later, found Bayne's friend and asked him about the lines quoted on that memorable day. All he knew of the poem was what he quoted and that it had originally been printed in the old Chicago *Times* and signed "Arrington." He had not committed to memory the entire poem. By his own admission he would not have recalled the lines or spoken them if it had not been for old man Falcon's strong emotions and Bayne's strong whiskey.

Mill's curiosity was piqued at this point. He started a search for the poem and its author. He soon discovered that the *Times'* files had been lost. He had, however, known a brilliant lawyer of uncertain habits who had been dead for three years by the name of Alfred W. Arrington. Perhaps, he thought, this could be the author. Mills, however, could find no one who had heard Arrington read the poem much less claim authorship of it. Finally, in his search he located Arrington's son. Unfortunately, young Arrington had no knowledge of the poem or his father's connection with it, if any. He suggested, however, that a poet-lawyer from Ottawa, Illinois, named Oliver C. Gray, might know something about the poem. This proved to be the key to the mystery. From Gray, Mills learned the whole story of the poem and its author. His hunch had been quite right. It was Arrington. But the story behind the poem was as interesting as the story behind the cargo of the *Mary Smith,* and not as disappointing.

In the early days of the Civil War, Alfred Arrington had strong loyalties to the South. As the war turned more and more against the Confederates, his deep sense of sympathy for the underdog and his love for a lost cause made him a rabid secessionist. Most people treated him with good-natured tolerance. In 1863, let it be remembered, it took more than a little courage to hold and express such feelings in the North. Arrington lacked nothing of courage. He wore his unpopularity like a badge of honor. Sometimes he wore a black eye to match his honor. The end of the war brought Lincoln's tragic death. The nation mourned, and hunted the assassin. John Wilkes Booth's name became a vile word. People screamed for vengeance. They soon had it. Booth met his death in a burning barn.

The night the news reached Chicago, a man with a pale face and disordered attire, drunk with alcohol and anger, rushed into the editorial rooms of the Chicago *Times*— a paper with strong copperhead tendencies. He gave the editors a poem dedicated "To John Wilkes Booth." He signed it Alfred W. Arrington. The next morning the poem eulogizing Lincoln's assassin appeared prominently on the editorial page of the Chicago *Times*. Later in the day Arrington, wanting more liquor, walked into the barroom of the Sherman House at Randolph and Dearborn Streets. Federal troops filled the tables and lined the bar. Many were happy about the capture and killing of Booth. They knew Arrington's strong feelings and excused them. That day, however, they had been drinking—perhaps too much. Besides, it was a different day. Arrington joined them in drinking several glasses of whiskey and then announced to all that he was going to recite an original poem. He jumped up on a table and started reciting the poem he had written the night before:

> Oh! Give him a sepulchre broad as the sweep
> Of the tidal wave's measureless motion;
> Lay our hero to sleep in the arms of the deep
> Since his life was as free as the ocean.
>
> It was Liberty slain that maddened his brain,
> To avenge the dead idol he cherished;
> So it's meet that the main, never curbed by a chain
> Should entomb the last freeman, now perished.

He dared break the rod of the blackamoor's God—
All the hosts of the despot defying—
May not dwell in the sod by a Nation's feet trod
That he shamed with his glory in dying.

Yes, hide him away from the sad eyes of day
In the coral of sea-green abysses.
Where the mermaidens gay as they fly through the spray
Shall purple his pale cheek with kisses!

As the ocean-streams roll from the Gulf to the Pole,
Let them mourn him with musical surges!
Let the tempest-bell toll the repose of his soul
More sublime than the sound of its dirges!

He has written his name in letters of flame
O'er the archway of Liberty's portal
And the serfs that now blame shall crimson with shame
When they learn they have cursed an Immortal!

With each of the words anger mounted in the soldiers at the bar. They sensed the meaning. When at the end he announced that the poem was dedicated to John Wilkes Booth, a roar went up from the soldiers. They dragged him from the table and hurled him to the floor. Arrington would have been trampled to death if it had not been for the quick intervention of the proprietor who grabbed him away from his attackers and shoved him out the back door. Apparently Arrington never again acknowledged the poem.

But that is not the end of the story. In 1866 he visited Texas. His pro-secessionist sentiments made him a welcome guest among the leading men of Texas. After that sojourn, he returned to Chicago and died, but the story of the poem did not die with him.

In 1888 a Texas paper printed the poem and erroneously credited it to Alexander W. Terrell. Five years later this same Terrell, prominent in public affairs in Texas, was appointed Minister to Turkey. In an attempt to defeat his confirmation in the Senate, his enemies reprinted the poem and attributed the authorship to him. The maneuver, however, failed. Terrell became Minister to Turkey. Significantly, the poem which was discovered in an abortive attempt to raise a cargo of whiskey near Buffalo, had in a sense come back almost to the same spot. For the President who appointed Terrell Minister to Turkey was Grover Cleveland, formerly Mayor of Buffalo and Sheriff of Erie County.

And that is the story of how a lost cargo of whiskey helped to find a lost poem dedicated to Lincoln's assassin. There will always be those of certain tastes who will never consider it a fair exchange.

FREE AS AIR

They all seemed free—as free as air
To gamble, fight, and drink and swear.

From *The Convention of Drunkards*
By Rev. Charles Giles
New York, 1840

OF SAND AND TIME

A bright moonlight streaked the lake water. It shimmered gently as the soft wind tried to spread its sparkling sheen over the sandy beach. Along the canal and river, dozens of grain elevators reached skyward like the towers and parapets of medieval castles. In the water the barks and schooners with sails furled rolled gently to the soft lullaby of a lake breeze. Here and there steamers with fires banked for the night seemed to be breathing slowly and contentedly in their slumber. On the other side of the river harbor, the oil lamps of the Canal Street groggeries painted grotesque shadows which danced crazily on the walls and the cobblestone streets. The drunken noises tried to reach across the river and canal to the south beach but the clear moonlight, the lake breeze, and the slowly moving creek seemed to filter out most of the animal-like noises leaving only the faint suggestion of sound—a pleasant background to the quiet of the south beach.

) 49 (

Across that beach this night, a lone figure hurried toward a darkened house that fronted on the lake. He pounded loudly on the door. After several minutes a light came to the window on the second floor. The window flew open and an angry voice yelled down. "What in hell do you want, man! Don't you know it's two o'clock in the morning?"

"Yeah, I know it is," admitted the voice on the lawn, "but I gotta see Charlie Payment right away."

"Oh, you do, do you? Well the Captain's sleeping and I'm not going to disturb him for the likes of you." With that, the man on the second floor slammed the window shut. As he turned from the window and started back through the hall toward his room, he saw the Captain in his nightshirt coming down the hall with a lighted candle in his hand. "It's all right, Jack. That voice sounded like Captain Hubert's." With that the Captain opened the window and holding the candlestick above his head hollered down. "That you down there, Tom?"

"Yeah, Charlie, I've got to see you right away."

"Sumpin' troublin' you, Tom?"

"Yeah, and it's mighty big trouble. Hurry up, willya, I ain't got much time."

"Well what in hell's wrong with you anyhow? The door's open, why don't you walk in?"

"I don't wanta come in, Charlie. I wanta talk to you out here."

"Okay, Tom, I'll be right down." Captain Payment thought Tom's behavior was very strange. He was not ordinarily so excitable or mysterious about his actions. As the Captain started down the stairs, he wondered whether his friend had been hitting the bottle. "No, that couldn't be it," Captain Payment mumbled to himself. "Tom never took more than one or two drinks and then only to be sociable with his crew. Matter of fact, that was one of the reasons why Captain Payment hired him as the skipper of his vessel after Tom lost *E. S. Bemis* in a wreck the year before. No sir, something must be very wrong with Tom to come calling at two in the morning." Captain Payment pushed open the door and walked over toward Tom standing in the yard. The full moon highlighted Tom's face; his eyes seemed to have a strange glaze. He looked at Charles as if he weren't really there. Beckoning him over, Tom whispered to him, "Charles, I just killed a man."

Payment stood there numbed by this blunt confession. "You're joking, Tom. How could you murder anyone?"

"I'm not joking, Charlie. I had a scuffle with some wharf rat in a tavern on lower Main Street; lost my temper; hit him over the head with a bottle."

"Come on, Tom, get hold of yourself. How can you be sure he was dead?" Charlie placed his two hands on Tom's shoulders as if to reassure him and then said, "Here, I'll tell you what I'll do. I'll walk over and see what really happened."

"No need to, Charlie. He's dead; I'm sure of it. Just as dead as the bottle he'd been drinking." Tom paused for a moment and then said, "You know, Charlie, there's a certain dumb look a man gets when he's dead. This guy had it." The tone with which Tom Hubert made this statement convinced Charlie that the man surely must be dead.

There was silence for a moment and then Captain Payment, looking straight at him and in reassuring tones said, "What do you want me to do, Tom?"

"I want you to get word to my first mate on the *Columbian*. I can't go over there because the Watch will be laying for me."

"You want me to go, Tom, is that it?"

"You gotta go for me, Charlie. It's my only way out."

"Okay, if that's what you want, I'll go in and dress. Be back in a minute." As Charlie walked back into the house, he was still trying to make himself believe that Tom had killed a man. Tom was his best friend. Only last Saturday,

Tom had had dinner with the Payment family in the very room through which Charlie walked on his way to the stairs. As he started up the stairs he remembered pleasantly how often he and his wife had visited Tom Hubert's family in Detroit. And he remembered the many times that he had raced his ship, the *H. S. Winslow*, against Captain Hubert's *E. S. Bemis*. After the *Bemis* went down, Hubert seemed like a lost soul—a Captain without a ship. Unless a person had been master of his own vessel he could never know the gnawing feeling a skipper gets when his ship goes down. It's like losing the most precious thing in the world. It's like losing the dearest member in the family. No wonder, he thought, Captains go down with their ships. In the long hitch, it's much better that way.

As Charlie started down the hall toward the door, he remembered how Tom looked that summer day in 1870 just after the *Bemis* sank. He remembered also seeing him a few days later sitting on the wharf gazing out over the lake as if he expected the *E. S. Bemis* to come sailing in as she had for many a year. As if it were yesterday he could remember that conversation. "Tom, I'm mighty sorry about the *Bemis*."

"Thanks, Charlie," said Tom Hubert, as he looked up from the wharf, "but it won't bring her back."

"I know it won't, Tom." Then Charlie paused for a moment and said, "You know, Charlie, the *Bemis* had the prettiest lines of any schooner in this harbor, unless of course it was my own *Winslow*."

Tom looked up at Charlie Payment. There was no humor in his face. "Look Charlie, I ain't in the mood for comparisons and I don't want to be reminded of the *Bemis*."

"Sorry, Tom, I meant no offense. I liked the *Bemis* and thought maybe you liked the *Winslow* too."

"Well I do but I just don't want to talk ships today," said Tom Hubert.

"Okay, Tom, if that's the way you feel. But I wanted

you to know that there's a skipper's job open. If you hear of anyone interested, let me know." Captain Payment turned and started across Water Street.

Tom jumped up from the wharf, started after Payment and said, "Come here, you old carbuncle. You know I'll die of plain dry-rot if I don't get a ship."

"You mean you'll take the job, Tom?"

"As of now, you've got yourself a skipper, Captain Payment." Tom stuck out his hand and Charlie took it.

That was a year ago. Tom stayed with the ship the rest of the season. Then this year he was appointed master of the *Columbian* which now lay in port. A better skipper, the *Winslow* and *Columbian* had never had.

"How could such a man be a murderer?" thought Charles. Whatever it takes to commit a murder, Captain Payment was sure Tom didn't have it. Maybe it was self-defense—that's it, self-defense. The drunk swung at Tom and to protect himself he hit him with the bottle.

By now Charles Payment was lacing up his shoes. That done, he put on his light jacket and started down the stairs as quickly as possible so as not to waken Mrs. Payment. As he passed the kids' door at the top of the stairs he stole a quick look and saw that his two boys were sleeping soundly in their snug harbors. Outside, Tom and Charlie started for Hubert's skiff which would carry them over the Blackwell Canal to the spot where the *Columbian* was moored.

For almost a minute, as they walked along, neither one said a thing. Then Tom started mumbling half to himself and half to his friend, "Charlie, why did this thing ever have to happen to me?"

"Take it easy, Tom. I've got it all figured out. He swung at you and in self-defense you hit him with the bottle. It was as simple as that. Self-defense!—A man's got a right to defend himself ain't he?"

"Charlie that would be all right, but it wasn't self-

) 53 (

defense. He was just sitting there drinking. Some uncontrollable urge seized me. It was as if someone else were making my actions for me. I picked up the bottle and slammed it over his head. Then I plunged the jagged edge of the bottle again and again into his head. He screamed, pitched forward face down on the table and then rolled over on the floor. His eyes were open and sort of bugged out. There was a frozen expression of terror on his face. Then the blood started rushing down over his face."

Charles took a good look at Tom again. He noticed that same dazed look in his eyes—the same look one gets when he's taken a hard right to the jaw. Then in measured words, almost not believing that he could be asking the question, Charlie said, "You mean to tell me, Tom, you killed a man in cold blood?"

"Well if that's what you mean by a cold sweat, yes I did."

"But Tom, how could you do such a thing?"

"I don't know, Charlie, but it's done and you've got to save me."

The two men had walked across the sandy waste which sloped down from the bank of the Blackwell Canal to the lake. At this point along the canal, the salt dock was located. Large sheds had been built on the dock to protect the salt from bad weather. Beyond these sheds lay the path to the rowboat Tom said would be waiting to take them over to the *Columbian* on the opposite bank. As they approached the sheds, Payment was perhaps a step in front of Tom Hubert. He could hear Hubert mumbling to himself how sorry he was for having committed such a horrible deed. Just as they walked into the shadow of the sheds, he heard Tom say, "Stop!" He wheeled about quickly and found himself looking into the barrel of a revolver. Tom Hubert's finger was on the trigger. Before Captain Payment could say a thing Hubert said in clipped words, "Payment, get down on your knees unless you want your brains blown out right away."

"Tom, what's the matter with you? Have you gone mad? Aren't you in enough trouble as it is, or is this just a bad joke?"

"This is no joke, Payment, and neither is this revolver. Now down on your knees and start praying. And Charlie,—pray good, because you only have two minutes to live."

"Now wait a minute, Tom."

"I said I'd wait two minutes, didn't I, Charlie? Say, that's pretty good, isn't it." With that Hubert pushed Captain Payment to the sand. "Now listen here, Payment, I warned you you've got less than two minutes to live. You'd better make your peace with God, because you're going to meet Him."

Charlie Payment knew Hubert meant business. The cold steel barrel and the look in his eyes convinced him that this was no joke. "Tom, for God's sake, what is the meaning of this? Are you going to commit two murders in one night? Put that pistol down and let's stop fooling."

"No, Charlie, not two murders, just one—yours. And you'd better start praying because your time's getting short."

"How can this be," thought Payment. "It must be a nightmare. Less than an hour ago I was sleeping in my bed. This must all be a bad dream."

"I don't hear you praying, Charlie. If you have any sins to confess, I will be your confessor."

Where the line is between hope and despair is difficult to know, but wherever it is, Charlie knew he had crossed it. He felt absolutely helpless—weak and drained. Think of it, he was about to die. For the first time in the last agonizing minute he began to think about that. He was going to die and there was nothing he could do about it. Die—he, Charlie Payment about to die. What was it they said "Ashes to ashes and dust to dust—" Just think, he had been born, lived, married, raised a family and now he was going to die. Just like that. Here on this lonely sand beach without his family about him. Without his ship under him he was going to die. He grabbed a fistful of sand and let it trickle out of his hand. Like the sand his time was running out. He was going to die. The more he dwelt on the idea, of dying, the more it began to intrigue him. Would the bullet hurt when it pierced his brain? Then a crazy thought. Would he hear the explosion or would he be dead before the sound reached his ears? He looked up at Tom whose face now wore an almost satanic expression. "You know I am without arms and within your power, so if you want to murder me I cannot prevent it." With that he closed his eyes and waited. It was quiet, it was very quiet. He could feel the blood beating in his temples. His mouth was dry and his throat almost closed. Droplets of sweat appeared on his face. Still nothing happened. It was quiet, so quiet he could hear the water gently lapping against the shore and still he waited and waited. "For God's sake, Hubert, pull the trigger and get it over with."

After an eternity Charles Payment felt Hubert grab him by the arm saying, "Get up and be quick about it. We're going across the flat and over the sea wall to the lake beach. It will be easier to dispose of your body over there." Still holding the pistol at his temple, Hubert then ordered, "Hold your hands above your head. Walk straight. One false move and you're dead."

Payment started to walk forward toward the sea wall. Hubert followed close behind. Beyond the sea wall the two had to walk close to several houses. Payment resolved to make a break away. He knew he could not turn around to see when the best moment might be. It would have to be a leap and a prayer. Then he said to himself, "This is it." With all the energy he could muster he sprang forward. He had not taken one full step before Hubert pulled the trigger. Charlie knew, for he heard the sound of the revolver hammer. It took him a split second to realize what had happened. He had heard the sound of the hammer but not the explosion.

Now he was running with all his might. Hubert was close behind. The next shot was not a dud. It creased the air so close to Payment's face that he could feel the wind from it. Stumbling and falling, but always moving forward. Ball after ball whizzed by him, kicking up the sand in front of him. Never had he run so fast. Finally he made the street but he didn't stop running until he was sure there was a safe distance between him and Tom Hubert. Then for the first time in an hour, Payment sat down. His lungs felt as if a hot poker had been thrust into them. His stomach was tied in knots. He was sick, very, very sick. He emptied the contents of his stomach several times over. When he was drained, he lay down in the sandy field close by the road. The cool lake breeze felt good on his face. All he could think of was how good it was to be alive.

Once again he grabbed a fistful of sand and let a thin strand trickle out of his hand. Now there would be more time.

DRUNKARD'S ODE

How well do I remember, 'twas in the late November,
I was walking down the street quite full of pride.
My heart was all a-flutter as I slipped down in the gutter,
And a pig came there and laid down by my side;
And as I lay there in the gutter, all too soused to even mutter,
A lady passing by was heard to say:
"One may tell a brute that boozes by the company he chooses."
Hearing this the pig got up and walked away.

UNKNOWN

Tale of the Pickled Porkers

TALE OF THE PICKLED PORKERS

South of Lake Ontario, in the northwestern section of York State, the ghostly shoreline of a prehistoric lake forms a ridge on which red men, and later white, have worn paths and built roads. Quite naturally, it is called "The Ridge." When the waters receded from this old beach, they left behind fertile fields, rutted with a few creeks and blotched with some swamps. Across these fields, the water had spread its rich silt along with a mixture of small stones and rocks, some rough and sharp, others water-washed smooth and round. These latter became the building stones for the sturdy and decorative walls of central York State's famous "Cobblestone" houses which give so much character to the Ontario country.

The real life of this country, however, seems to have moved along The Ridge. In proper sequence, it has felt the soft step of the Iroquois, the beat of horses' hoofs, the roll of stage and wagon wheels, and now the speed of the motor car. Today, as the cool breeze from the present lake sweeps over the plain and across The Ridge, only in the inner ear of imagination, keen and finely attuned, can the ancient waves of the lost lake be felt and heard. To learn of man-made times, however, there is needed only an attentive eye and appreciative ear. Old-timers with good memories and better imaginations can still recall, for those who will listen, stories of The Ridge when the wagon wheels rolled over the road to the Niagara River.

Located as it is, midway between the Niagara escarpment on the south and Lake Ontario on the north, The Ridge became a land route to the West for the pioneers before the Erie Canal provided a waterway westward. For those along the highway, who from their windows have watched history go by their door, The Ridge is also a road back to the past; its taverns the stopping off places to tell its tales.

The pioneers built these tavern-inns at convenient stage-coach distances most frequently at crossroad "corners" west to the Niagara River. Some of these still stand. In fact, some are still lived in. One such is located at Warren's Corners; that is, the map calls it Warren's Corners and for good reason. Despite this almost official recognition, how-ever (and I suppose it is duly and officially registered and recorded elsewhere), some natives there-abouts think it ought to be called Forsyth Corners for what they consider even better reasons. But that is all part of the story.

At the back of this tavern the ground falls away sharply. In wet seasons the low land is swampy. About the center of the backyard area a huge four-trunked willow tree spreads its cover over much of the yard.

One afternoon I stood there drinking in the charm of the surroundings—(that's about the only kind of drinking that tavern had seen since 1825, if the stories I had been hearing were true).

"Quite a tree, isn't it?" said a voice which startled me.

I answered, "Yes," almost automatically as I turned my head quickly toward the direction of the voice.

"This your farm?" I asked the approaching figure.

"You bet it is. Own land on both sides of The Ridge."

"Well, it certainly looks like rich land to me, although I am really no expert in such matters," I said.

"It is rich," he readily agreed. "Rich for crops," and then with a smile, which crept slowly up his cheeks, "rich for stories, too. I guess since I own the land, I rightfully own the stories, too. What do you think? At least, I ought to have the right to tell them. The fact is, stories are really no good unless you share them with someone else."

"I certainly agree with you on that," I said.

"Take that tree over there, the one you were looking at.

Must be over 100 years old. Notice its four trunks. It's no ordinary tree," he insisted.

"No it certainly isn't. It's a real beauty, and huge too," I said.

"I don't mean that exactly," he spoke seeming to feign impatience. "I mean it just ain't an ordinary tree."

"Well," I said, somewhat amused, "what is it if it isn't a rather good ordinary tree?"

"It is a buggy whip," he shot back at me. "At least, it was a buggy whip."

"A buggy whip?" I repeated in amazement.

"Yes," he explained, "an honest-to-goodness, overgrown buggy whip, come to life. As I get it from those who have passed on, this was one of the important stagecoach taverns in the old days. Often the drivers would come out in the back here to stretch their legs before they went into the tavern to bend their elbows. One driver apparently stuck his whip in the muddy ground and went in to have just one for the road. Apparently, he had more than one (road-dust being what it is), and when he left he forgot his whip. No one thought any more about it until a month or so later. Then one night, as the tavern owner threw out some food scraps and slop (as he was accustomed to do each night) he noticed it sticking in the ground. Something drew him over to the whip. As he approached he could hardly believe his eyes. The whip had apparently taken root. It was actually greening and growing. And that's how a buggy whip grew up to be that four-trunked willow over there.

"At least," said my friend with a chuckle, "that's the story they tell hereabouts."

"Quite a story for a tree," I said. "Certainly shows the fertility of the soil along The Ridge." I was about to add "and the fertility of imagination" when he interrupted my thought by saying,

"Well, yes, in a way it does, but that's only part of the story. You see, it has never been clear to me from the story whether the buggy whip grew before or after God visited the tavern."

This stopped me cold for a moment and I must have stood there with my mouth slightly ajar.

"What do you mean," I stuttered, "before or after God visited the tavern?"

"Well, maybe," the farmer said, "I had better tell you the whole story from beginning to end. And I guess I ought to start at the beginning. 'In the beginning'—say, that does fit in rather well when you are talking about a visit from the Lord, doesn't it? In the beginning," he started and then interrupted himself by saying, "well, if we are to begin that way, we ought to go around to the front of the house and really start from the beginning."

The house from the front still retains some of the general appearances it had as a tavern. Modifications have taken place on the inside but very few on the outside. The house, or tavern as it used to be, is now located on the southwest corner of the junction of Stone Road, Ridge Road, and the Lockport-Cambria town line. It all began when John Forsyth, his wife and two children left Batavia in 1805 with an ox-sled loaded with household goods and food, at the head of a procession of pigs, sheep, and a cow. Mrs. Forsyth and the two children rode the horse while Forsyth himself followed on foot at the rear of the wagon train to prevent any straggling animals from getting lost. It must have been a lonely trip, for they saw only three or four families along the way. When he came upon this very spot he knew it was the place for him. Like other pioneers, before or after, he followed the pattern of claiming the land. He drove a stake into the ground. This was now his land, his home and his future. But it was still a real wilderness. He set to work to clear the land. He built a log cabin for his family and himself and a log shelter for the animals to protect them from the wolves which infested the region. Nevertheless the wolves killed all the sheep the first year.

Snakes caused trouble too. To the north and east of the Forsyth cabin, beaver dams plugged many of the creeks that flowed to the lake, thereby swamping much of the land. So thick were the rattlesnakes, that Forsyth, whenever he cut swamp grass for his livestock, wore leather boots to protect himself on the outside from snake bite and took several stiff shots of whiskey to protect himself on the inside. The snakes even crawled into the house. On her return to the cabin one day, Mrs. Forsyth found a rattler curled up beside her child who was asleep on the floor. Quickly, quietly, she picked up the axe standing near the door, moved toward the snake, raised her arm, and brought down the axe right behind the head of the snake and a fraction of an inch away from the child. Then she sat down to catch her breath. The child slept on.

The Forsyths met their daily problems well. Slowly, pioneers settled the country. In 1808 a surveyor laid out Ridge Road. With the possibilities of a road junction in the offing at this point, John Forsyth built the frame tavern through whose door we were about to pass.

"That stone," said the farmer turning partly around as he crossed the porch, "is the same one that DeWitt Clinton stepped on when he stopped at the tavern on his trip to the West in 1810. You recall he was trying to get the lay of the land for his famous ditch."

To an old "canawler" like me, it seemed almost sacrilegious to step where the "patron saint" of the Erie Canal had stepped almost 150 years ago. I did it but with reverence.

"And here," said my friend, pointing to a slit in the right side of the porch, "is where the stagecoach mail was pushed through."

We entered. Once inside and seated comfortably, he told the stories of the tavern as generations had told them before. Beginning in 1816 the stagecoach made regular stops at the "Corners" with mail and passengers. Forsyth himself, however, never lived to see this. In fact he died

June 2, 1812, just before the War of 1812 began. The war brought that tavern a thriving business, and only one slight interruption in its service. This occurred on December 19, 1813, when the British raids across the Niagara River drove practically all of the settlers out of the western half of the county. The widow Forsyth sent her children to her brother east of Batavia while she and the other two remained at the Corners. The Ridge became a road of safety for the fleeing people. Unfortunately, it also served as an avenue of desertion for some regular army and some militia men. As a result, an Ezra Warren, sergeant in the regular army, along with two other soldiers, was stationed at the tavern in order to watch for stragglers and deserters. In a short time Warren fell in love with the widow Forsyth. Following his discharge from the Army, even before the end of the war, Warren returned and they were married. After that the place became known as Warren's Corners although there are still those who insist it should be called Forsyth Corners.

The war's end saw growing numbers of pioneers on the move westward through York State. Conestoga wagons lumbered over the Genesee and Ridge Roads carrying an old world westward to the new—to the lake country and beyond. Politicians renewed agitation for a canal; legislation followed; several surveys were taken, and finally the digging of the canal itself was begun. Meanwhile, Ezra Warren did well at his tavern on The Ridge.

Along with the completion of the canal and the great thrust of people westward, a strange phenomenon occurred. An outburst of highly charged religious emotions engulfed central and western part of the State. Millerism, Mormonism, Spiritualism, Utopianism, and Anti-alcoholism swept over the land like wildfire. In time the reform movement left behind "a burnt over region" of spent emotions. But while feelings burned brightly, many people were fired with the passion of zealots. The "fire" reached Warren's Corners one night in 1825.

That night Mrs. Warren persuaded a reluctant Ezra to go with her to a service at the Methodist Church at the "Corners" to hear a hell-fire, brimstone, total-damnation preacher curse the sinful evils of liquor drinking. It was said he held the power to open the heavens and loose the wrath of God with his fervent voice. Understandably Ezra was none too eager to attend the service. After all, he liked his whiskey and made a good living selling it to others of like mind. But in the end, he went anyway.

When he walked out of the church that night, he was not the same man who had entered earlier. He was deeply troubled. His soul seemed to be wrestling with the habits and desires of a lifetime. Man does not change easily the old patterns of living. For hours, disturbing thoughts kept him from sleeping. Finally he fell asleep. This was even more frightening. Suddenly he sat up bolt-like (or was he dreaming?). A shaft of light flooded the room blinding Ezra for a few moments. Out of the light came a deep and commanding voice. A body-outline took shape. By now Warren had fallen to his knees prayerfully. He stiffened in terror. He was struck dumb. The Voice told him to go forth throughout the land, to preach the Gospel and the evils of liquor to whomsoever. Then the figure placed his hand on Ezra's head in a gesture of blessing and baptized him. Ezra in his own mind had been reborn. He took the name "Father Warren." From then until the day he died at age 90, he refused ordinary baptism, claiming the "Lord had baptized" him.

The next morning like a man possessed, Ezra went down to his liquor cellar below his bar. One by one he rolled his liquor barrels over the stone floor toward the rear. He pulled the latch string on the door, opened it and pushed them out to the top of the gully. Then with his axe he smashed in the barrel heads. Out spilled whiskey, brandy, and brandied cherries. Ezra stood, axe in hand, and watched the barrels empty themselves of their evil contents. At the end (like the barrels) he felt purged and clean. Then he went inside and closed his bar forever.

Now in those days of unfenced farms, farmers let livestock wander about the fields, roads, village streets, and yards. The law required only that they be registered with the town clerk. This particular morning, as usual, the pigs from the adjoining farms made their way over to Warren's swampy gully for their daily meal of tavern garbage and slop. With all the greed of pigs, they swilled the liquor and lapped up the brandied cherries. Their normal appetites must have been even sharper than usual that morning. Soon the spirits took effect. The pigs started to wobble but they kept on drinking. Finally one by one they fell over in a drunken stupor and lay contentedly in the swampy ooze. When Warren came out later, he found the pigs lying in the gully not dead, as he first thought, but dead drunk. He set out immediately to tell his neighbors to come, bring their "mud-boats" and get their drunken pigs out of his yard.

"Well, that's it," said my story teller, "that's the Tale of the Pickled Porkers."

Then after a moment, he turned and said, "Now you can see my confusion. If the liquor spilling happened just before the willow whip incident, it probably wasn't just the fertile ground that caused the buggy whip to take root and grow but the special irrigation Ezra gave it that morning after the 'Lord's visit.' For the fun of it I like to think that it happened that way. One way or the other that whiskey-brandy-swamp water drink must have been about the most powerful shot in York State."

"Well," I agreed partially, "it sure must have been powerful stuff. But don't be too sure about your comparison. I've heard that Erie 'Canawlers' used to claim 'Canawl'

water and whiskey (Erie Brand of course) was so strong
the breath of it would open all the locks at Lockport. But
fair minded as they were, I'm sure they would agree with
you that, if your swamp water and whiskey from The Ridge
were strong enough to make the blood run hot in hogs
and the sap run high in a dead dry buggy whip, it would
have been a fit companion for their 'Canawl' water and
whiskey—but only as a chaser."

THE ERIE IS A RISIN'

For the Erie is a risin'
An' the whiskey's gittin' low,
And I hardly think
We'll git a drink,
Till we git to Buffalo.

TAVERNS AND TRAP DOORS

Captain Ben Cole yelled from the bridge to hold fast. The vessel nestled up slowly to the central wharf; out flew the hawsers. Quickly the hands snubbed them to the dock iron. As the steam was cut, the vessel stopped shuddering and rode softly with the gentle roll of the inner harbor water. Safely docked, Cole went back into the pilot house, took out the roster to see who had ship watch the first night ashore. It was young Mike. The youngest hand always had first watch and this was the first time Mike had shipped out.

With roster in hand, the Captain started down to the

crew quarters, called Mike over and reminded him that he was to stay aboard the first night. Mike, of course, had been expecting this duty. Still, it was difficult for him to conceal his disappointment in not being able to go ashore with the rest of the crew. All during the trip the older hands had been telling him over and over the story of the infamous Buffalo waterfront.

Captain Ben read the disappointment in Mike's face.

"I'm staying aboard, son," said Captain Cole. "I'll sit it out with you. Mebee I'll even entertain you with some of my biggest lies." Then turning to the rest of the crew who were making ready to hit the gangplank, Cole shouted, "Now mind the rest of you fresh water salts, stay clear of those 'blackleg' gamblers. They'll skin you for every cent I've paid you. This cesspool has the crookedest crooks on the lake. Worst 'blacklegs' in any port."

With this, the whole crew snorted with laughter but there was none who doubted what he said.

"Hey, Captain!" shouted one of the hands, "you told us to stand clear of the 'blacklegs.' Don't want us to stand clear of the shapely white legs too, do you?"

"Mark me, mateys," Cole said, shaking his finger in warning, "stay clear of the white legs in this port too. They're worsen the blacklegs."

"Captain, now you know that ain't fair," put in the mate, "the female white legs ain't near as bad as the ornery male 'blacklegs.' Lookee here, the 'blacklegs' take all your money but they don't give ya a damn thing in return. Now the gals take your money, but just think what they give in return."

The crew folded in laughter. When the Captain had quieted his belly laugh to a gentle chuckle, he pointed his pipe at the young sailor and said, "Laddie, you're right. They sure do give you sumpin in return. Sumpin you'll try the rest of your life to get rid of. Better stay clear of them white legs too."

"Now, Captain," said the mate, "you yourself told us that Buffalo is a 'lay-over' port. Well, that's just what we're fixing to do plenty of."

Still laughing, the men scrambled up the ladder to the deck, across the gangplank, and onto the wharf. Captain Cole and Mike stood on the bridge watching them as they darted in, out, and around the baggage piled high on the wharf. Soon they lost them in the milling mob of canawlers, lakers, and immigrants who clustered on the waterfront streets and wharves.

Cole continued to watch and chuckled a little to himself. Mike, who had been a little bewildered by the banter in the crew's quarters, drew his chair up close to the Captain and said, "Captain, is Canal Street as bad as you and the men make it out to be?"

"Son," replied Cole, "it's worsen. Here, let me fill my pipe, and I'll tell you all about it. But believe me, laddie, this is not one of my yarns. Fetch me that lantern over there so's I can get a light."

Soon the Captain was puffing away contentedly. He knew the waterfront and he loved to talk about it.

"Mike," the Captain said, "let me tell you about the waterfront I knew as a lad your age. When I first came to these docks, everything was in the hands of the canawlers and a sailor cut no figure a'tall. As the sailors grew stronger, there were more and more fights for supremacy. Believe me, Mike, these were real fights—Spanish knives, stones and fists. Buffalo was a hard place in the early '50s. In fact, a life didn't count for very much on the Buffalo waterfront. There were worse joints around Canal Street than you would believe."

Mike stopped him for a moment and said, "How about the police, Captain Cole?"

"T'warn't any police in those days," Cole added, "only a few watchmen. Often as not they were worsen the murderers and thieves. Most of them kept their noses out of the waterfront and vice held sway unchecked. Fights and cutting frays were nightly occurrences, and the denizens were as evil a lot of crooks as have ever been collected in one place. Mike, the mining towns in our days are no worse than this waterfront. Gangs of sailors hung on every corner spoiling for a fight. Those were the days when ole Mother Carey's dance hall was famed throughout the land, and was the scene of many a fight. In the dark alleys and slips, murders occurred for which no record can be found in the criminal annals of the city. The 'Points' were let alone by the authorities and thievery, licentiousness and vice more than flourished in that awful hotbed.

"Never forget one experience I had, laddie. I was no older than you and for awhile, I thought that was as old as I was ever goin' to be. Shortly after I'd been given my own ship, I went ashore one day with my first mate. I had a roll of money with me but never gave it a thought. The mate proposed to get a drink in the place next to ole Mother Carey's. I agreed and we went in. I was young then and did not know the town very well. After we had the drink, he said 'Come here, Cap'n.' I followed his beckoning finger. He opened a trapdoor in the back of the saloon. I thought I might as well see what was there. We went down and got into a passageway that led about fifty feet. Then we came to a heavy oak door about four inches thick. The mate rapped a peculiar knock on the door and it opened. Inside was a room about twelve feet square. In one end was a bar with five or six black bottles stuck up on it, and at the other end was a table where three men sat playing cards.

"The door closed behind and I knew I was trapped. I had heard of the place. It was one where they fed drugged drinks to the suckers that got in there, rolled them and then poked them out through the slide with a stone around their necks. When they were found, it seemed as though they had committed suicide by jumping into the Canal. I knew where I was and I thought I was a goner. The door was bolted on the other side and I heard it slip into the catch.

"Well, sir, I began to buy them drinks. I made out that I was an awful drinker and said that I could drink the whole lot of them drunk. I poured out big tumblers of the stuff, and poured them down my neck on the outside, instead of the inside. I was fairly ringing with cheap whiskey. They drank the stuff and got paralyzed. I pretended to be boiling drunk and pretty soon everyone except the bartender was stiff. I made him take drinks with me till he got pretty well under. Did you ever see one of those Spanish knives? We all used to have them in those days. Stuck up your sleeves, you know, and bound round your wrist with a thong. I took this out and grabbed the bartender—I was a husky lad in those days—I told him I would cut his throat if he didn't open that door. He finally gave the signal and I got out of the place soaked with whiskey. Spent seven dollars for those drinks I bought those cusses, but I was mighty glad to get out of there. You see, the mate knew I had money and he got me in there."

Mike, who was hanging on every word, asked, "Whatever became of the first mate, Captain Cole?"

"Well, sir, I saw him a few years ago in Chicago. After I fired him, I don't think any respectable Captain ever hired him again. When I saw him, he was beggin'—a regular 'wag,' Mike, as I told the men, there ain't no 'blacklegs' anywhere like those on this waterfront."

"But, Captain," Mike put in, "what about the gals—the white legs the boys were talking about? Ever had any experience with them?"

The Captain sucked in slowly and deeply on his pipe. His eyes looked out over the Canal Street district and he said thoughtfully, as he patted Mike on the knee, "Plenty, laddie, plenty—but they're all trade secrets."

TALL TALE TELLER

I landed in Buffalo about twelve o'clock,
The first place I went to was down to the dock,
I wanted to go up the lake, but it looked rather squally,
When along came Fred Emmons and his friend Billy Bally.

Said Fred, "How do you do, and where have you been so long?"
Said I, "For all the past fortnight I've been on the canal,
For it stormed all the time, and thar was the devil to pay,
When we got to Tonawandy Creek, we thar was cast away."

"Now," says Fred, "let me tell you how to manage wind and
        weather.
In a storm hug the towpath, and then lay feather to feather;
And when the weather is bad, and the wind it blows a gale,
Just jump ashore, knock down a horse—that's taking in the sail.

"And if you wish to see both sides of the canal
To steer your course to Buffalo, and that right true and well,
And if it be so foggy that you cannot see the track,
Just call the driver aboard and hitch a lantern in his back."

HAY ON THE SUN

In slanting beams that silvered the dust in the air, the sun filtered through the thin morning haze which had settled lazily on the quiet waterfront. Under the dockboards, the harbor water made suckling noises. Atop the wharf with a snub post for a pillow and a hat on his face, Fred Emmons soaked up the sun and snored out his contentment. Most of the snores were full-throated and nose-muted, but intermittently what started out as a well-rounded snore, would get snarled up in his throat pipes and die in a characterless gurgle. This abortive snore usually set up a mild convulsive shaking which travelled quickly through his body and ended up in a wheezing cough which almost, but not quite, succeeded in arousing Fred Emmons from his sleep.

Fred Emmons obviously took his Sundays seriously. For this, he made no apologies. The Good Book said it was a day of rest. Fred meant to rest. He felt he deserved one in seven. During the other six days he practiced hard a profession peculiar to a port like Buffalo. Some from Delaware Avenue might smile at his work being dignified by the word profession but Fred thought it was just that. Officially, (if the city directory could be considered official) Emmons was listed as a steamboat and hotel agent. He preferred to call himself a General Solicitor. Among the soap-lack fraternity of the waterfront, however, he and his cronies were popularly known as "runners." And well might they be called that because that is exactly what they did. As one waterfront wag put it, the runners put the hustle in the harbor bustle.

Originally, in stage coach days, these runners brought passenger and freight business to the line of their hire. With the construction of the canal and the creation of steamboat lines, the stages began to die and these agents transferred their allegiance to the place where the money was. Noisy and loud as the waterfront was, high above the usual noises could be heard the voices of the runners singing the praises of this hotel or that steamboat. Living by their wits, competition made them sharp-tongued, sharp-eyed, and fleet afoot. In their own way, they were artists. Today they would be dignified with the title "advertising executives" and would be in demand for newspaper, radio and television work. The stories about these runners were legion. They themselves were legends.

The runner extraordinary of Canal Street was Fred Emmons. No one ever admitted outdoing or outwitting Emmons—at least to his face. His boundless energy was equalled only by his imagination. For example, in the early

1830s, the steamboat *Peacock* burst its boiler a few miles from Buffalo. Many were drowned and many more scalded. Thousands who heard or read about the story hesitated about travelling on steamboats. Not long after the horrible accident, Emmons, plying his trade, approached a group of emigrants and urged them to book passage aboard his nice new steamboat which was about to embark for Detroit and intermediate points. After Emmons had made his pitch, an elderly lady in high dudgeon spoke up, "I don't like steamboats; you bust your bilers and scald folks." "Oh!" countered Fred, "my dear madam, ours is a new steamboat, constructed on a new principle, not one of those high pressure boats like the *Peacock* but a low pressure engine." Then looking her straight in the eye and measuring each word, Fred said, "We use nothing but cold water. In fact, we never let it come to a boil." Emmons as usual got the business.

But not all the stories about Emmons concerned deals on the dock. One night after work, as he made his way home through the dark streets that served the harbor, a robber stepped from between two buildings leveled a fist at Emmons but missed. Fred quickly turned around and said, "What do you want?" The would-be assailant, slightly abashed, said, "Your money or your life." To this Emmons replied, "See here, stranger, I haven't any money, but if you will step around with me into 'Perry's Coffee Shop,' I will give you my note for ninety days." Apparently the robber had a sense of humor for no harm came to Fred.

Emmon's light touch even reached into the Mayor's office. Samuel Wilkeson, builder of the harbor and first mayor of Buffalo, is supposed to have borne the brunt of one of Emmon's quips. It seemed that a new steamer had been built in the Buffalo harbor. It was magnificent to behold. Apparently perfect in all parts, it floated gracefully as a swan. Its speed was unmatched. There was only one thing wrong with the ship, the engineers couldn't make it back up. The problem was finally placed in the Mayor's office. Emmons was summoned as he was then acting as police chief. After the Mayor had stated the problem, Emmon said quickly, "Well, your Honor, I think that if you just make a mustard plaster out of some Pelix White's salve and put it on her stern, that will draw her backwards as lively as anything I know of." The Mayor reportedly never asked Fred Emmon's advice again.

Perhaps as Emmons snoozed and snored on the dock that Sunday morning, he dreamt of some of his many experiences. At any rate, when he awoke, he stretched out his arms, emitted a loud yawn, rubbed his eyes, pinched the back of his neck and slowly surveyed the waterfront. What to do? Fred missed the crowds, the noise and the general weekday hubbub. He liked Sundays but he missed people. Perhaps, he thought, something was going on uptown. The thought interested him enough to get him up to his feet and start him walking toward the Terrace.

The canal boat families were sunning themselves on top of the barges. Some were doing a little fishing. All seemed to be relaxing. Not much fun here, thought Fred. So he crossed the bridge over the canal and made his way up Main Street toward Church. In front of the Episcopal Church was a huge sundial. The dial had a special appeal for Fred. Shortly after it had been constructed, Fred applied for the position of Keeper of the Sundial. In support of his application he submitted to the Board of Aldermen a universal petition filled on both sides with names that Emmons had clipped out of the pages of the directory and pasted lengthwise on the petition. In his petition he promised the people that if he were appointed he would construct a shed over the dial in order to protect it from the sun.

Fred parked himself next to the dial. Since most of Buffalo passed that way on Sunday, Emmons thought it would be the most likely place for him to receive a dinner offer. There were few people on the street. Church was not out yet, so Fred bided his time. As he slouched against the dial with hands in pocket, he noticed a farmer with a load of hay making his way down Main Street. To Emmon's experienced eye, the farmer looked like a "green one." As he drew within hailing distance, Fred yelled, "Hello there! What you got aboard?" The farmer reined in a bit, looked at Fred for a moment and said, "Hay." "Hay?" Fred said in mock surprise. "Don't you know you have laid yourself liable for arrest?"

The farmer's face blanched in shock and disbelief, but he finally managed to ask how that could be.

"Well," said Fred, "when you enter the city, you are supposed to have your hay weighed. But if you will wait for just a minute, I will fix everything for you. If you will bring your wagon over here in front of the weigher, I'll check it for you."

Fred motioned the farmer to come over in front of the sundial. When the wagon was centered in front of the dial, Emmons took out a piece of paper and a pencil and started jotting down a few figures. Every so often he looked up at the dial and then wrote some more figures on his paper. Finally he looked up at the "green one," handed him the paper and said, "There, I guess that will do. Here is your certificate and that will cost you 25 cents." The farmer reached quickly into his pocket, fished out a quarter, and handed it over to Fred.

"Thank you," said Fred, "that does it nicely. Thank you and good day."

The farmer gave a giddap and the wagon rolled on down Main Street. Well, thought Fred, as he flipped the coin in his hand and watched the wagon disappear over the Terrace, there's more than one way to make hay while the sun shines on Sunday.

PUT THE "BUFF" IN BUFFALO

Fifteen years on the Erie Canal.
I eat my meals with Sal each day,
I eat beef and she eats hay,
She ain't so slow if you want to know,
She put the "Buff" in Buffalo.

"Low Bridge, Everybody Down"
Words and Music by William S. Allen
F. B. Haviland Publishing Co.
New York City

THE MAN WITHOUT A SLEEVE

Weather-wise, it had been a rare day. A day with a smile on its face. Everyone and everything seemed to like it. On the towpath even the mules stepped livelier. Their skinners sang much faster but no sweeter. On deck, the captain wore a grin as wide as an open lock. Even the Erie Canal wore its best. The water seemed to blend the deep blue of a spotless sky with the earth-green of growing things. As the barge moved forward, pushing aside the water, silver streams ran off to the side, breaking for a moment the solid water color and then just as quickly melting back into skyblue and earthgreen. It had been a June day and rare was, indeed, the word for it.

William Nowlin drank in the beauty. The breeze gently spanked his cheeks as he stood on the bow of the barge looking southward toward Buffalo less than a mile away. He felt that this was really it. This was the great moment he had hoped for, planned for, and worked for. The Nowlins were headed west. Here was the great adventure. Looking out on the horizon south and west, a feeling of destiny gripped him. It was more than a personal feeling. It was something outside of him and his family. He felt a part of something great. He knew now that it had been in the air like a contagion since they had first boarded the barge at Albany. No one tried to talk about it. Probably no one could. It was just there. You knew it.

Nowlin's eyes studied the men standing on the topside of the barge. His mind took in the wives and children in the cabins below. They and the Nowlins were a part of a great mass movement westward. They came from the hinterlands of Europe and from the tidelands of America; from old England and New England. They were new America on the march. They and, more especially, their children were the bright, brave New World.

They were the pioneers.

These thoughts crowded his mind as he looked westward across the Niagara River and watched the setting sun paint the sky a beautiful afterglow. For some minutes, Nowlin's eyes remained fastened to the western sky, hypnotized by the changing colors. It was fascinating to watch the dark blue of the night sky press down on the orange-red of the fading day sky. Suddenly, his reverie was broken by the all too familiar yell of his little girl. "Daddy, Daddy." Nowlin turned around just in time to catch her under the arms as she jumped at him. Playfully he swung her out in wide circles so that her legs flew out over the water. Her little nose wrinkled as she giggled in the delight of danger. She staggered a bit as Nowlin set her down on her feet. Pointing a warning finger at her, which he waggled good-naturedly under her nose, he said, "Now see here, young lady, you'd better rein in a little when you come running toward the edge of something. You might trip and fall some day."

"But, Daddy," she protested, "I knew you would catch me."

"Oh, you did, did you? Well sometime I might fool you and then what'll you do?"

"Get wet," she laughed. Her laughter tinkled like gay little bells.

"That's exactly right," Nowlin said. "Now tell me, if you have any breath left, what's all the excitement about?"

For a moment the girl had forgotten what she was excited about. Then suddenly it came to her like the rush of water when a dam bursts. The words tumbled out of her mouth so fast it sounded to Bill Nowlin like some kind of gibberish.

"If you really want me to know what you want me to know, you had better check rein your tongue a bit."

The little girl laughed at her father's words and then with a little less excitement, but still with a high pitch of expectancy in her voice said, "Well, where are they?"

"Where's what?" her father questioned.

"Where are the Buffaloes?"

"What Buffaloes? What are you talking about?" Nowlin asked.

"Why, I heard the big people down below talking and they said we would see the Buffaloes in just a few minutes."

Nowlin chuckled, "So that's it." Crouching down beside her and slipping his arm around her tiny waist, "I'm afraid, my dear, they didn't say 'Buffaloes,' they said 'Buffalo.'"

"Oh, all right, where's the Buffalo then?"

Nowlin smiled again. "Baby, I'm afraid you're in for a disappointment. Those people down below were talking about Buffalo, the city, not the animal. So far as I know, there are no Buffaloes in Buffalo."

The little girl tried to push back the cloud of disappointment that darkened her face but it wouldn't budge. "I don't thing it's very nice to call this place Buffalo when there aren't any Buffaloes here."

Nowlin smiled at his little girl's protest and said, "Well, dear, it hasn't always been called that. Matter of fact, the captain told me just a few minutes ago that the original settlers called it New Amsterdam, since the area was originally owned by a Dutch Company. Would you like New Amsterdam better?"

"Well, I think it's a much better name than Buffalo, especially since there are no Buffaloes here. I can't see why they changed the name."

"Well the good Yankees hereabouts probably thought that the name 'Buffalo' was more American than the name 'Amsterdam.' And, since the creek which now forms its harbor was so important in the development of the city, they probably decided to name it Buffalo after Buffalo Creek."

"Well, but Daddy, how did . . ."

Nowlin did not let her finish the question. "I know; you want to know how the creek got its name. The captain told me he didn't rightly know. Some people claimed that there were really Buffaloes here at one time. Others say that the stream was named after an Indian. Still others contend that Buffalo was the sound the Indians made when they tried to pronounce the French name for the creek."

Nowlin looked at his little girl. He could see that he hadn't lifted her expression of disappointment. Picking her up so she could see better, he pointed to his left and said, "Over there is the creek—Buffalo Creek. You can see the masts of the various vessels. Some place yonder in that tangled mess of masts is the *Michigan* and we'll be aboard her tomorrow headed west."

These words sent a new thought racing across her mind. As if by magic it erased her downcast look and once again her eyes danced.

"Oh, Daddy," she said, squeezing him tightly and nuzzling her face against his neck, "could we sleep on the boat tonight?"

"Would you like to?"

"Very much."

"Well, I don't know, my dear," he said, letting her slide down gently. "We'll have to ask your mother and see what she says." Then pointing to the stairs he said, "Why don't you go below and get her? We'll be docking in a few minutes."

The little girl was off like the wind, her blonde curls flopping against the back of her neck. In a few minutes she was back hand in hand with her mother.

"Well, my dear," said Nowlin as he took his wife's hand and slipped his other arm around her, "the first leg of our trip is just about over. They'll be 'pike-poling' the canal boat around the corner into Commercial Slip in just a moment. Is everything shipshape below deck?"

"Yes, Bill, everything is ready to be taken off."

"The willow basket—where is it?"

"It's safe. Timothy is watching it."

"We have to be very careful with that basket. We can't afford to lose it."

"I know, but Timothy's a dependable boy. Nothing will happen to the willow basket with him watching it."

"Look quickly over there, dear," Bill Nowlin shouted and pointed at the same time. "You can see the harbor and, oh!—look!—doesn't that say 'Michigan' on that ship straight ahead?"

Mrs. Nowlin squinted her eyes a bit, "Why it does say 'Michigan'!"

"Well, that's it! That's the boat we'll be on tomorrow. Isnt' she a beauty?"

"Well, I wouldn't know about that, Bill, but it does look strong enough to stay afloat and that's what I'm interested in, staying dry inside and out."

"What do you say, Mother, shall we sleep aboard her tonight? I know the kids would enjoy it."

"Well, I suppose it would be fun," said Mrs. Nowlin as

she tried to think the problem through, "but don't you think we had better save our money and take a cheaper place? We're going to need every penny to keep going our first year. 'Member how the Smiths had to give up and come back after their first year. I don't think I could face the folks back home."

Nowlin tightened his arm around her just a bit and with the other arm patted her gently on the forearm. "Well, my dear, maybe you're right. We probably will get a better night's sleep in a public house here on the waterfront." Bill went over to the railing, eyeing carefully the establishments along Commercial Street.

"Well, from the noise and confusion round abouts I don't think we'll get very much sleep in a boarding house *or* aboard the Michigan. Have you ever seen anything like it?" Mrs. Nowlin asked.

"What did you say?" Bill asked as he turned and cupped his ear.

"I said, 'Have you ever seen anything like it?'" Mrs. Nowlin shouted.

No, Bill Nowlin had never seen anything like it. It seemed as if the roads of the nation crossed here where the Erie Canal joined the Commercial Slip and the Buffalo Harbor. On both sides of the canal, two and three deep, were canal barges. Commercial Slip was completely clogged. One could walk dryshod from one side of Commercial Slip to the other. All along the line big, burly Irishmen with burnt brown skin carried bags, barrels, packages and household goods out of the holds of the barges and piled them high on the wharf. In some places along Commercial Slip, whose one side acted as the wharf, freight was piled above the second story of the buildings which lined the side opposite the canal. As the stevedores struggled up the narrow, ribbed gangplank with their loads, you could hear a thick Irish brogue demanding a clear road. Along the street people pushed and pulled and tried to keep from being swept along in the opposite direction. Serious minded clerks, giving the impression of importance, wore serious expressions on their faces as they clutched business papers in their hands. They ran swiftly in and out of the various business houses and commission rookeries where the commercial business of the port was transacted.

Nowlin had never seen anything like it. The other ports along the canal had had an exciting hustle and bustle about them, but here on the Buffalo waterfront it seemed that all the noise of the whole canal had been brought together in one continuous wild sound that seemed to pulsate against your ears. There seemed to be no order in the seething mass of humanity which filled Canal and Commercial Streets.

To Nowlin it seemed as if every language and every accent could be heard in the swirling, Babel-like confusion. Reaching out high above the crowd noises, he noted, were the voices of the "runners" or "solicitors" (as they were professionally called) trying to get various passengers to stay at this hotel or to take that boat. In the melee, coats and dresses were torn, sometimes the baggage of immigrants ended up in one place and they in another. The runners were indeed, a breed apart.

Nowlin noticed another waterfront breed. These characters, members of the "soap-lack" fraternity, leaned up against the taverns and saloons that lined the street. They were the drunks, the beggars, the thieves, the blacklegs and prostitutes, looking over the new arrivals to pick out the most likely-looking suckers. Nowlin made a mental note to be thankful to the Almighty if they got out of the Buffalo waterfront with their lives and their money.

Nowlin broke himself away from these thoughts for a moment and said, "Well, Mother, I guess I'll go down and get Timothy and the baggage."

Minutes later the four Nowlins found themselves standing on the wharf listening to the runners singing out the praises of their respective hotels and boats. Then they made their way along Commercial Street, down Canal Street to Maiden Lane. There, Nowlin saw a house which offered rooms at what he thought was a reasonable rate.

"Mother, how does this look to you?" Nowlin asked.

"Well, I don't know, my dear, it doesn't look too clean but it is cheap."

"Well, I guess we can stand it for one night. I'm so tired I could sleep any place. Let's go in."

In the dingy entrance just off to the left was a little table that had once been an elegant piece of furniture but like the fat woman who sat behind it, the table had fallen on evil days. Her blotched face had been made uglier by liberal doses of paint in the wrong place. As Nowlin looked closer at her pimpled face, however, he realized that there could be no right places on her face. Nowlin asked her if his family could rest in that room for a few minutes while he went down to the Michigan to make sure of his arrangements.

Soon after Nowlin left, the woman came over toward Mrs. Nowlin, reached down to the willow basket as if to move it a little, then lifted it and said knowingly, "You must have plenty of money, your basket is very heavy."

Mother Nowlin stood dumblike. She just looked at the woman who now quickly turned on her heel and walked out of the room with the air of someone who suddenly remembered that she had something that needed to be done quickly. Mrs. Nowlin was frightened. She felt surrounded by evil. But she kept her fear away from the children. She thought her husband would never return. When he finally did enter the door, her fear melted away but the concern was still there. She told him immediately about the woman and the willow basket.

"William, I'm scared," she said, "I don't like the idea of staying here, especially with that five hundred dollars in silver in the willow basket."

"Well, my dear, I think we're stuck. I've checked at the

other places on my way down to the steamer. They're all filled. I even asked the captain of the *Michigan* if we could stay aboard that boat tonight, but he told me that was out of the question. They were making some minor repairs and no one would be allowed aboard until morning. So I guess we'll just have to worry it out here."

Nowlin no more than finished that sentence, when the fat woman returned. Bill asked if they might have a sleeping room with three beds. "Well, mister," said the woman as she tried to fit her backside into the chair behind the desk, "we're pretty well crowded, but I do have a small room on the third floor with three beds and you can have it if you want it."

"Well, I guess we haven't much choice. We'll take it."

With that Nowlin turned, walked back to his family, picked up the baggage and led the way upstairs. It was three flights up through a narrow, rickety staircase. On the third floor they found the door to their room. It opened into a dark, dismal, windowless room. The door through which they entered was their only entrance and exit. Bill Nowlin did not like the looks of things, but he also kept his fears to himself.

"Well, kids, we'll all have a big day tomorrow, so we'll all pile in and get some sleep." Mrs. Nowlin helped the children with their clothes, tucked them into bed, and put the willow basket with the silver in between them—she thought that would be the safest place.

After looking over the situation downstairs, to see if everything seemed safe, the older Nowlins went back up to their room and prepared for bed. Though they were gone only a few minutes, the children were sound asleep by the time they came back.

Bill and his wife had not been long in bed when he thought he heard footsteps outside the door. Before he could get up, the door opened a crack and the light cut the darkness of the room like a knife. A man with a candle tiptoed into the room. Nowlin started to get out of bed, but Mrs. Nowlin put a restraining hand on his arm as if to say, "Quiet, don't jump him yet." The man with the candle went to each bed to see who was in it. Bill Nowlin's bed was last. As the intruder went around his bed, Nowlin sat up bolt straight and asked the man what he was doing in the room and what he wanted.

"I'm looking for an umbrella," said the man with the candle.

"Here, I'll give you an umbrella," said Nowlin and with that jumped from the bed, grabbed at the man and caught hold of his sleeve. The man tried to jerk away but Nowlin had a firm grip on his sleeve. As he lunged forward, the sleeve ripped at the shoulder, but the man kept running out of the door and down the stairs as fast as he could go. Nowlin sat on the edge of the bed with the sleeve in his hand.

Nowlin and his wife knew that there would be no sleep for them the rest of the night.

Turning to his wife, Bill said, "I'm going to put my knife above the door just in case our friend returns."

Everything remained quiet for about three hours. Then once again the Nowlins heard something.

"Do you hear what I hear?" said Bill Nowlin.

"Yes, it sounds like footsteps doesn't it, but without shoes."

"How many do you think there are?"

"Sounds to me like two or maybe three."

As they got to the top stair, Nowlin picked up a chair, held it above his head and stood at the side of the door. As soon as Mrs. Nowlin heard the latch turn, she yelled so that they could hear her, "John, have the pistols ready! The moment they open the door, shoot them." Mrs. Nowlin's stratagem worked. The door closed and the footsteps descended the stairs quietly and quickly.

Bill Nowlin put down the chair, threw his arms around

his wife and planted a big kiss on her mouth. "Aren't you the cool one, my dear? What would I ever do without you?"

"Well, I did it, my dear, so that I wouldn't have to do without you. I figured that with that chair and your knife, you probably would have killed one of those men and the other two would have killed you."

"Well, maybe, my dear, they won't come back anymore."

"Don't be too sure of that. I think we'll have to stand guard all night."

"Yes, I know we will," said William Nowlin.

They both settled back to wait. In just about three hours they heard footsteps again. As the door opened, Mrs. Nowlin said, "All right, my dear, be ready now and mow them down the moment they burst open the door."

Again they went away only to return just before dawn. If possible, this time they were even quieter than they had been before. Again Nowlin took his place beside the door with the chair in hand. Just before they started in, they were greeted again by Mrs. Nowlin's voice. "All right, John, shoot the first one that enters. We'll blow them to kingdom come."

For the fourth time the scheme worked, the thieves left. Mrs. Nowlin breathed a sigh of relief, her husband put the chair down and sheathed his knife, the only weapon they possessed. That was the last visit of the night. Soon Bill could hear noises out on the street. Since there were no windows in the room, it was the only way they could tell it was time to get up. They quickly got the children out of bed. After dressing and getting the children dressed, they collected their baggage and started down the long flight of stairs to the rooms on the street level. Nowlin walked over to the woman behind the desk and complained about the man who had entered the room. He held up the broadcloth coatsleeve as evidence. The women said that it must have been the old man who usually slept in that room.

"Well, from now on, you'd better be careful to inform

him when the room is occupied. And I'm telling you, if I find a man around here with one sleeve I'm going to give him the beating of his life."

Nowlin never found his man and he never forgot the story of his one-night layover in Buffalo. Often in later years, when he entertained his friends in his Michigan home, he told all who would listen (and even some who wouldn't) the story of their escape from the man with one sleeve.

MURDER A DAY

It is an exaggeration to say that there was a murder a day on the Buffalo waterfront during its hey-day. Probably there was not more than a murder every other day. Some statistics show that seventy to eighty percent of the major crimes in the United States occurred along the Erie Canal and Canal Street in Buffalo between 1830-1835.

DUBLIN, MUGGER, AND THE COTTON-HOOK MAN

During the upheaval of the Civil War period, a ruthless clique of Buffalo waterfront desperadoes organized themselves into a gang of beach guerrillas. Led by four unholy watermen named Dublin, Jimmy the Cotton-Hook Man, Leary Reedy, and Billy the Mugger, they terrorized the Buffalo waterfront. Their lair was "Michigan Island" in the middle of the inner harbor.

Like Sandytown, another rivermouth area, the spot was protected by a kind of water ditch, and, like Sandytown, this became a squatter haven. The water moat surrounding the area gave medieval protection so dearly loved by the disreputable waterfront characters whose lawless activities found little appreciation among the police watch or the "Respectability" of Buffalo.

Buffalo's original harbor had consisted of a creek that snaked its way into Lake Erie from the rolling hills to the southeast. Western bulk and eastern package freight, together with the greatest mass movement of people the world had ever seen, flooded into Buffalo with such tidal proportions, after the opening of the Erie Canal, that agitation started at the end of the first decade to increase the inner-creek harbor area.

After much pressure and time, work began on what soon became known as the City Ship, or Blackwell, Canal. This artificial waterway ran almost parallel to the creek, thereby doubling the space of the inner harbor. The cutting of this canal created an artificial peninsula that local habitues of the waterfront dubbed "The Island" because, for most people, the only access to the spit of land in question was by bridge or rowboat. This became the guerrillas' hideout.

At first the guerrillas operated on a small scale, boarding vessels at night and taking only plunder that they could carry in their arms. With success, they grew bolder, until finally they attacked vessels in force, driving off the crew and systematically carrying off the cargo. They had no trouble in peddling their loot along Canal Street. In those days, the police force, or "watch" as it was called, was so small that it could not match the strength of the pirates. By simply blowing a whistle, Dublin, or any of the other leaders, could quickly gather a force of one hundred men, armed and capable of resisting any police attempts to capture them. For years, after each raid, the gangsters would retire to their island lair and there, fortified by the natural protection of their position and whiskey, they defied the police to attack them.

On several occasions, the police, despite all the precautions taken by the land pirates, did manage to capture some of the leaders. Even Dublin served time in the Buffalo jail. It happened this way. One night he was leading his guerrillas aboard a schooner loaded with staves. While supervising the operation of heaving the staves overboard onto a tug, which the gang had captured earlier, Charles and Dan D'Arcy, police officers, crept quietly aboard the vessel. "Cotton Hook" and "Mugger" were both aboard the vessel topside helping Dublin transfer the cargo. So quickly and silently did the D'Arcys steal up on the gangsters that they were taken by surprise. Dublin showed no fight. The others, too, seemed paralyzed.

As soon as Dublin recovered his senses, however, he broke for the railing and dove over it into Buffalo Creek. Since the D'Arcys were more interested in the capture of Dublin than the others, they jumped over the railing and dropped like a couple of lead plummets on Dublin, who was thrashing in the water. Dublin gave a good account of himself until a water uppercut took the fight out of him. The D'Arcy boys dragged his almost lifeless body back to shore. Meantime, of course, the rest of the boys escaped. Dublin was committed to jail for a year and, on his release, returned to his old lair on the island.

The year brought many changes. Many of the younger and more respectable men on the island signed up with the Irish regiment formed in Buffalo. The Beach Guerrillas, however, would join up, collect the fifty-dollar bounty, and then jump their enlistment. When Dublin returned, therefore, he found his comrades, "Cotton Hook," Leary Reedy, and "Mugger" still operating. One sunny day not long after his release, Dublin sat on the shore bank of the island watching the schooners and other vessels come and go. He mentally noted the size, cargo layout and position of the various boats that pulled in and docked. Suddenly he spotted a trim schooner that caused him to stand up to get a better look. She was loaded to the gunwales with a mixed cargo. Her deck furniture, done in natural dark wood, with the oblong cabin, indicated rich interior comfort. With two hundred and fifty feet overall and a white hull with a gold bead around it, Dublin thought her the trimmest craft ever to moor along the Island pier. Never had Dublin's eyes seen such graceful lines on a sailing craft. And his eyes had seen almost every vessel then sailing the Lakes. On her stern panel, in proud lettering, was the name, *Mercedes* of Saginaw. Dublin watched her captain pull her into her proper slip. Then he dashed off to find the Hook, Mugger and Leary.

By the time Dublin reached the shack, he was out of breath. "Hey, Mugger," he called out as he reached the shack, "are the others inside?"

"Sure now, and Dublin, you wouldn't be a-runnin unless the Watch were after the likes of us."

"Wrong, ye Killarney fool," Dublin called out. "But come in. 'Tis a beauty I've spotted." Mugger followed Dublin inside where Cotton and Leary were sorting the loot gotten the night before.

"Listen, ye good-for-nothin' Shanty Irish," Dublin started out good naturedly.

"Shanty, maybe, but jailbird like you be—no," Cotton Hook greeted him. And with that, they all roared. Cotton Hook brought his arm down so hard on the table that Leary had to help him pull the hook out.

"Boys," Dublin said, still bubbling over with enthusiasm, "the Saints be praised, our ship has come in."

" 'Tain't the first ship that came in that we haven't made like our own," said Leary.

"This be different, lads, she's a beauty. Name's 'Mercedes,' " Dublin explained.

"And so we'll be boardin' her tonight and takin' off her cargo and 'twill be so dark she will look like all the other vessels in the harbor," said Cotton Hook.

"Yeah," offered Leary, "vessels at night be like women at night—they all look alike."

Dublin was not to be swerved from his original idea and so he continued trying to outline the plan. "Lads, we board her tonight but we ain't takin' no cargo."

"See here, Dublin, have you seen the Leprechauns, and gone clean daft? What do you mean, take no cargo? How's the likes of us to live?" shouted the Hook.

"Here now," Dublin said in a confidential tone. They all leaned their heads closely toward Dublin and listened while he laid the plan for their new adventure.

That night the guerrillas boarded the vessel, plucked off the crew, hog-tied them and dumped them on the wharf. Once in control of the ship, Dublin signaled to the tug operated by the guerrillas. A line was thrown out and the tug pulled them out of the Buffalo channel and a mile up the Lake. Here they cast off the line to the tug and the guerrillas on the tug made their way back to the schooner in a rowboat.

Meanwhile, the guerrilla crew aboard the schooner set to work repainting the *Mercedes* in open water. Since the morning sunlight was warm and bright, the paint dried quickly. They painted out the old name, Mercedes, and replaced it with the name Annie, a young love of Dublin's. With the painting done, the crew took advantage of a stiff breeze that bulged out the sails and carried the *Annie* to a safe bay on the Canadian shore before midnight the following night. The *Annie* had sailed into the night and into history.

Many an old captain told of seeing the *Annie*. Many described, in glowing terms, her pirate adventures on the Great Lakes. How she could steal into lonely ports, especially along the Canadian shore, raid vessels docked there, and be away before sunrise. Many Lakemen believe that the *Annie* had a part in the attempted capture of the vessel

Michigan in 1864. Still other sailors liked to tell of the important part that the *Annie* played in the Johnson Island plot to rescue two thousand Confederate prisoners on that Island in Sandusky Bay. But all this is in the realm of legend and fantasy because no one really knows.

What bold adventures befell Dublin, the Hook, the Mugger, and Leary may never be known. Should ever the log of this vessel be found—there would be a story equal to any pirate story of the high seas—the story of the *Annie* and her crew of Buffalo pirates.

THE IRISHMAN AND THE FALLS

As the Irishman looked at the Falls, he turned slowly to his companion and in a level voice thick with brogue said, "Faith, and what's unusual about this. Indaid, Ireland too has water that runs down hill. Now, if you can show me some water that runs uphill . . ."

Sam, Sam, the Jumpin' Man

SAM, SAM, THE JUMPIN' MAN

From the day Father Hennepin first described Niagara Falls, people the world over have come to gaze on its wondrous beauty. Many who have looked upon this beauty have felt a hypnotic power drawing them ever closer to the waters. Standing near the edge of the brink where the waters break out of the rapids and drop in a mad torrent over the 150 foot cliff, they have felt the pull of this magic spell most strongly. Some who fix their eyes steadfastly on the water as it curves over the cap rock, have found the mysterious force almost irresistible. Some even find it necessary to turn their eyes away. A few have been known to walk into the rapids and be swept to death. Others seem to feel a desire to pit their puny strength against the colossal power of Niagara. That many of these attempts have been ludicrous makes them no less tragic, for Niagara does not always stand for such humiliation. Exhibitionists have walked over Niagara on tight cables, flown under its bridges in planes and even rolled over it in barrels and rubber balls. In fact, one man even tried to jump over the falls. His name was Sam Patch.

It all began in 1826 at the other end of the state in New York City. Sam started jumping from the mast heads of ships anchored in the North River. His passion for notoriety encouraged him to risk his life in even greater jumps. As his reputation spread and the crowds grew larger, Sam tried higher masts. The day came when there were no higher masts in the North River. So he began to look around for new heights to conquer.

At the western end of the state, especially at the Falls, hotels and shopkeepers needed publicity. Now that the Erie Canal made transportation across the state comparatively easy, they wanted to lure people to the Falls. These entrepreneurs had read with the interest borne of money the newspaper stories of Sam's jumpin' feats. Soon arrangements were made between them and Sam to jump the Falls.

In September, 1829, widespread coverage was given to the announcement. It became the chief topic of cracker-barrel conversation whenever people gathered at the general store. Many allowed that it just couldn't be done. Arguments grew heated. Betting was heavy. While it had to be admitted that he had successfully jumped a number of times from great heights into the North River, his detractors quickly pointed out the difference between the calm waters of that river and the turbulent waters of the Niagara River at the foot of the Falls. Through all the loud doubt, Sam remained confidently calm and cool. To those who pointed to their head in a knowing gesture, Sam replied in priceless prose, "Some things can be done as well as others."

At Niagara, preparation went forward. A large platform projecting out from the Biddle staircase was constructed 125 feet above the water. Interest mounted. People from all over made arrangements to be on hand to watch "Crazy" Patch jump. Finally on October 6, 1829, the day had arrived. When all was ready, Patch climbed the ladder to the platform. All eyes were on the tiny figure atop the aerial stage. Many wondered if some things really could be done as well as others. There was no doubt in Sam's mind. To show his utter contempt for the danger, he danced a jig and sang a song.

> I wish I were in Buffalo,
> Good friends along with me
> I'd call for liquors plenty
> Have flowing bowls on every side;
> Hard fortune never grieved me—
> I am young and the world is wide.

Then Sam took another swig from his flask of rum and concluded

> Good liquor in a poor man's house,
> Is a pleasing thing to view.

As he finished his song, he stepped to the edge of the platform and, without hesitation, jumped. His body shot through the air toward the water 125 feet below. All the way down he managed an erect position. He cut the water feet first and disappeared below the surface. As if they were under the water themselves, every one seemed to be holding his breath. When his head bobbed to the surface all seemed to exhale a sigh of relief. Sam had conquered the Falls. He was a hero. When the man in the rowboat picked him up and asked him how he was, he said, "It's like I told you, some things can be done as well as others. Now give me a swig of whiskey to take the chill out of my bones."

According to the story, Patch remained in the Falls for a few days and made a second successful leap, just to show the doubters that the first was not an accident. Offers now poured into Sam asking him to appear here and to jump there. He soon announced that he would jump the Falls at Rochester. The scene was much the same as it had been at Niagara. Only this day, as he stood atop the platform overlooking Genesee Falls, he sampled the flask too heavily and too often. He was very drunk. If anything, he showed more bravado than at Niagara. After he had finished all his preliminaries and the flask, he stepped to the edge, spread his arms, and jumped off. As he fell through the air, he waved his arms wildly. Partway down, he lost his balance. His body flopped crazily in the air. When he struck the water, it tore his arms out of their sockets and broke his body like a toothpick. People looked on in frozen terror. It was Sam's last jump. Sam had learned that some things can be done, but not always as well as others.

WATER, WATER EVERYWHERE

When England was outfitting her Lake Erie fleet, which eventually met defeat at the hands of Perry in the Battle of Lake Erie in 1813, the Admiralty sent over to all the lake ships water casks for carrying fresh water. So strong was the tradition of salt water sailing, that the Admiralty did not realize that a bucket over the side of the boat would have tapped an almost inexhaustible supply of fresh drinking water.

On one occasion a crew of old salts returned to their ship after a long pull in a rowboat under the burning sun almost perishing from thirst. They had never thought of tasting the cool pure water which their oars were every moment splashing and flashing in the sunshine.

Forty Years of American Life
By Thomas L. Nichols
Pages 96-97

FRESH WATER AND FREE WINE

In the early forties of the last century, shipping on the Great Lakes out of Buffalo was riding a crest of unprecedented business. Shipping companies should have been making money but they were not. A price war was on. Competing lines ran steamers alongside the rival vessels, slashing prices at every port in a wild endeavor to secure the business offered. Travelers took advantage of the rate warfare.

Each steamship line had its own set of "runners" who worked the docks attempting to secure trade for the lines they represented. As the battle for business grew in intensity, it challenged the ingenuity of the most imaginative "runners" and captains. Armed with advertisements and speeling out unfounded claims, "runners" would attempt to persuade the travelers, first verbally and then physically, to take passage on the vessel which they represented. Frequently, several "runners" would pounce upon some hapless prospective traveler and succeed in tearing off most of his clothes. For years the city attempted to abate this nuisance but without success.

Immigrants ignorant of English and baffled by the customs and manners of this rough inland port, became easy prey for the slick wharf salesmen most of the time. The price war, however, had now given the traveler a temporary advantage. By September of 1842, prices had fallen so that it was possible to book passage from Liverpool to Detroit for seven dollars. The *Journal of Commerce* quoted a price of four to five dollars for emigrant passage from Liverpool to New York in the finest ships afloat. From New York to Buffalo that year, travelers could purchase transportation for one dollar and fifty cents. It had even dropped as low as one dollar and twenty-five cents. A dollar more would take the west-bound emigrant from Buffalo to Detroit. Added all up, it meant that Europeans could pass from their shores far into the interior of America for seven dollars.

The *Commercial Advertiser* of 1842 estimated that provision for the ocean, canal, and lake trip would cost about seven dollars. By adding a dollar more for emergency, the entire cost including food, transportation and incidentals would amount to about fifteen dollars. "There is no use calling," said the editor of the Buffalo paper, "upon past ages to come and see what is doing now. They would not believe it if they saw it."

Low as the prices had dropped, however, the bottom had not yet been reached. One day a man asked Captain David Wilkinson of the steamer *Commodore Perry* the price of cabin passage to Detroit. Wilkinson quoted him an amount which was considerably less than one-half the price of the regular rate. Anxious to please the prospective passenger, he invited him aboard for a drink at the ship's bar. Despite the pleasantries of Wilkinson's hospitality the traveler could not be induced to book passage.

A little later, while the Captain was walking along the wharf near his vessel, he again met the stranger who informed him that a rival steamer had offered to carry him to his destination for nothing.

Not wishing to be outdone by the rival line, Wilkinson turned to him and with a gesture of great magnanimity said, "Oh well, if that's the case, I'll carry you for nothing and board you. You will go with me, won't you?"

"Well, I don't know," came the unexpected answer, "I think his wine is preferable to yours."

BUFFALO GALS

As I was lumb'ring down de street,
   Down de street,
   Down de street,
A handsome gal I chanc'd to meet;
   Oh! she was fair to view.
Buffalo gals, can't you come out to-night?
   Can't you come out to-night?
   Can't you come out to-night?
Buffalo gals, can't you come out to-night?
And dance by de light ob de moon?

I ax'd her would she hab some talk,
   Hab some talk,
   Hab some talk,
Her feet covered up de whole sidewalk
   As she stood close to me.
Buffalo gals, can't you come out to-night?
   Can't you come out to-night?
   Can't you come out to-night?
Buffalo gals, can't you come out to-night?
And dance by de light ob de moon?

I ax'd her would she hab a dance,
   Hab a dance,
   Hab a dance,
I taught dat I might get a chance
   To shake a foot wid her.
Buffalo gals, can't you come out to-night?
   Can't you come out to-night?
   Can't you come out to-night?
Buffalo gals, can't you come out to-night?
And dance by de light ob de moon?

I'd like to make that gal my wife,
   Gal my wife,
   Gal my wife,
I'd be happy all my life,
   If I had her by me.
Buffalo gals, can't you come out to-night?
   Can't you come out to-night?
   Can't you come out to-night?
Buffalo gals, can't you come out to-night?
And dance by de light ob de moon?

(Sung by Christy's Minstrels)
Canal Street, Buffalo

The Poets and Poetry of Buffalo
By Edward Christy
Page 15

Kitty on a Pedestal

KITTY ON A PEDESTAL

Canal Street in particular and the Buffalo waterfront in general always wore the carnival air of a holiday. On holidays, therefore, the festive spirit knew no bounds. Of all the celebrations, none received the attention and treatment reserved for Independence Day. This holiday traditionally began on the second and lasted through the fifth. The days were filled with activity the clock around; the celebrants were filled with black strap and rot gut.

To mark the day as something special, tavern keepers brought in thousands of maple trees and stuck them in the ground. As if by magic, it touched the area with a bit of nature, normally lacking. Viewed from the upper terrace, the waterfront took on the appearance of a maple forest. The extremes in decorations during this period were matched only by the decor of the participants. The canawlers and sailors, who lived a lusty, brawling life, demanded entertainment to match.

As the Fourth approached, captains aboard lake vessels and canal boats bent their efforts to reach the waterfront in time for the fun and festivity. Drinking bouts, among other forms of indoor sports, were the order of the day. Rival crews tried to out-drink each other. The best bouts, however, were those between canawler and laker. For no respect or love was lost between these groups.

As soon as the crew had their ship fast at dock, off they went to their favorite haunt, which would be one of the many concert halls which flourished on the waterfront during the '70's and '80's. At the corner of Canal and Commercial Streets, many found the Only Theatre to their liking; the Olympic Theatre on Erie Street appealed to others. There were enough on Canal Street to appeal to the most discriminating taste of the watermen. Upon entering these concert halls through swinging doors, customers would find a bar which extended the length of the hall. At the far end away from the door was a small stage lighted with kerosene lamps. Along the side of the tavern or hall, opposite the bar, were booths where girls entertained the men who could pay the price. About fifty tables on the open floor provided places for those who could not afford the luxury of a booth. In some of the concert halls, customers sat on long benches on the back of which were small ledges. Waiters selling drinks and cigars would slide them along this ledge to the purchasers. So adept did these saloon salesmen become, that they could stop a drink in front of the prospective buyer.

Owners during the holidays usually tried to out-do themselves with entertainment. Unless the entertainment was out of the ordinary, however, the sailors were content with black strap and women. In the drinking bouts, one table of sailors might challenge a table of canawlers in the same tavern. Under the watchful eye of several impartial observers, the drinking would begin. Careful count was kept of each shot drunk by the participant. If one member of the team could no longer sit up at the table, his team mates would place him gently on the floor next to the table. According to the rules, he could still participate so long as he could open his mouth and swallow. His friends therefore, would continue to pour the liquor into his mouth. When both eyes and mouth finally closed and the participant was completely paralyzed, the tavern bouncer would drag the drunk off the floor into a special room where the "stiffs were dumped" like ten pins after a strike. The game proceeded until only one man remained. That team was then declared the victor. The tavern, as a reward for such outstanding performance, would buy the victor a drink.

On occasion, the professional entertainers managed to steal the attention of the crowd away from these drinking bouts. On the Fourth of July, 1881, word spread quickly through the infected region that Kitty O'Neil would do her famous dance that night. As the hour approached, waterfront characters pushed their way into the tavern where she was scheduled to dance. By the time Kitty began her dance, the spectators had packed themselves in so tightly that, as the drunks passed out from the influence of heat, liquor, and lack of oxygen, they remained in a standing position propped up by the tightly packed mass of humanity about them. There in the center of the theatre, atop a white Grecian pedestal, stood a beautiful young girl, whose lithe body would carry her to the top of the entertainment world. When no other person could be packed in, the dance began.

The dance was most difficult and made more so by its being performed atop a pedestal which measured only twelve inches in diameter. For one hour and twenty minutes, Kitty danced. She danced in the nude. No one moved. No one could move. When the dance was completed, and Kitty had made her bows, the doors of the theatre-tavern burst open. The compressed mass of humanity exploded into Canal Street. The applause and roars of the audience were punctuated by the thud of the dead drunk bodies as they hit the floor after their human props had been removed. It was some time before the tavern could sweep the human debris into the sobering room to make way for the paying customers.

The Buffalo waterfront took its Fourth of July seriously.

He is not drunk who, from the floor,
Can rise again and drink some more;
But he is drunk who prostrate lies,
And cannot drink or cannot rise.

Thomas Love Peacock

GOD'S WATERS

Oh Lord! I'm free. That little boat that brought me
here is going back to get my brothers.—Back and forth,
Oh Lord!, back and forth to freedom. It's God's waters
that flows both ways to get us and bring us to freedom.

FREEDOM IN THE WOODPILE

In the years before the Civil War, it is said that some four thousand slaves moved out of the northern port of Pultneyville, N.Y., across Lake Ontario, to Canada and freedom. Many were the stories behind the escapes—as many perhaps as the slaves that gained their freedom. Out of their escapes came the story behind the vulgar phrase "Nigger in the Woodpile."

According to some of the people in the village of Pultneyville this is the way it all happened one particular night (leastwise this is the way they told it to me).

It was that kind of night when dark clouds scudded across the moon, smudging it with ugly figures which the wind quickly washed clean again. A clod of people not distinguishable in the brush and shadows, waited for the cloud-darkened intervals to slip forward to the next cover. As the eye accustomed itself to the dark, one man among the group could be seen leading the way. Minutes before, they had all left the dusty road which had brought them from the southern part of New York State. Now they picked their way along a secret path, holding the branches each for the other to keep them from snapping in the person's face next in line.

Like hunted men, they moved quietly, nervously,—never quite sure. They threw haunted glances over their shoulders whenever an unfamiliar sound broke the night air. The leader, apparently knew his wood. Without false step or wrong direction, he brought his people to a spot where a large canoe nestled under the bank of a stream he called Salmon Creek. Now, all answering to a silent arm motion, they stepped into the canoe (a large one of the freighter variety) settled themselves, trimmed their weight for balance, and at the command, pushed off from the bank into midstream. Expertly turning the paddle for more power and less noise, the man in charge cut the water rather than broke it. The boat slid forward down the middle of the narrow winding creek. The water folded smoothly in behind the canoe.

A soft breeze shook the leaves. Willows and silver poplars caught it with a sharp high pitch-like tingling bells. The other trees harmonized with a deeper more mellow rustling. A flash of light would burst out, as clouds occasionally brushed past the face of the moon. Through the breaks in the trees, it streaked the creek with a shimmering silver and lighted the faces of the men in the boat. The paddler's face seemed to reflect more light than the others. No wonder. Close inspection showed his skin to be white;

the others black. Such momentary glimpses, like flashing pictures, made the darkness that followed deeper than before, and through it all, the same awful quietness.

The canoe moved on along the narrow pathway of water, and overhanging branches scratched against the men and the boat. Suddenly a crunching sound broke and startled the silence. Motion froze; everyone stiffened; no one breathed; everyone looked—listened intently. The black men turned quickly and instinctively to the paddler. After a moment of tight concentration, his body relaxed, his paddle motion resumed. Thus reassured, the others started breathing again.

"A woodchuck," he whispered in relief.

What a pity, he thought, after all these long miles of hardship and escape, if these poor wretched souls were now to be captured so close to freedom's shore.

The minutes and quarter-hours slipped by under effortless stroking. The creek curved gently northward through the woods to Pultneyville. Soon at a sharp right-angle turn, the white man reached out, grabbed a branch, pulled the boat over to the shore. He crawled out of the boat and scrambled up the shallow bank. There for a long time he lay, belly down, awaiting a signal from one of the three houses whose yards backed onto the creek.

Idly—as they waited the long minutes in the canoe—one of the Negroes, ever so softly, stripped off a little piece of bark from a bank tree, handled it fondly in the cup of his hand for several minutes and then, almost in reverence, dropped it into the water.

With a faint smile and almost a murmur, he thought, "Go down to the lake, little boat, go down to freedom."

For a few minutes the bark strip floated toward the lake in the general direction the canoe had been travelling. The Negro soon lost it in the darkness.

Minutes later, still gazing hypnotic-like toward the water, he wondered whether his boat, like himself, would ever reach Canada. Huddled in the canoe, he bethought himself as tiny and as helpless as the little piece of tree bark on the water. Still lost in his reverie, he suddenly thought he saw what looked like the same strip floating back. The clean, cream-like inside of the strip had caught the light.

"No, no!" he thought almost aloud, catching himself just in time, "It couldn't be the same piece."

Intently, he watched it disappear. Sure enough, a few minutes later, the little bark returned once again moving in its original and, what he thought, its right direction.

For a long time, with gnawing fright, the Negro watched the ebb and flow of the water and the bark. The more he watched, the more terrified he became.

"A spell, the water's bewitched," he thought. Fear of capture dried his throat. Every small sound was thunderous. Even the moon seemed crazylike with mysterious figures dancing on its face. He gripped himself tightly to regain his courage.

Just then, the awaited signal from the house appeared. Cautiously, they all climbed out of the boat and up the bank, following the leader. The man who had been frightened looked back at his piece of bark floating back and forth in the stream. Prayerfully to himself, he said, "No time now, Lord, to be afraid."

They crossed Pig Lane, moving toward the backs of the three houses. One stood in front of them; the other two were off to the left. Farthest to the left was a cobblestone house; next, a large, white dignified New England-type frame house; and finally, the one toward which they made their way, a small, white frame salt-box type house. In later years, a brick addition in the front, topped by a cupola and a widow's walk, would cause this house to be known as the "Little Brick"; but now it was just a salt-box. All three of these houses backed on Salmon Creek, faced on Washington Avenue, and overlooked Lake Ontario. Much of the village activity centered here. These houses occupied the three original lots of the village of Pultneyville—Pultneyville which once promised to be a large port east of Rochester, and in the years before the Civil War still held its head high with such hopes.

Through its harbor, farmers and commercial merchants shipped produce—fruit, fresh meat, potash and wood, carted and floated in from the interior of the state. Steamers made four regularly scheduled calls a week. Schooners arrived frequently and unannounced. To many, during the critical prewar days, Pultneyville was more than an active and promising port. It was an underground railroad station—the last station on the land route from the South—the jumping-off place for Canada and freedom. This "runaway" route reached northward from Bath on the Cohocton River, along Canandaigua Lake crossing the east-west Erie Canal, Seneca Turnpike, and the rail lines. Finally, and on occasion, the underground railroad left the wagon road as it approached Lake Ontario and took to Salmon Creek, which flowed northward to Pultneyville. Other fugitive slave routes, some perhaps more important, carried the slaves northward to Buffalo, Rochester, Oswego, and the St. Lawrence River. Freedom lay across the rivers and the lakes to Canada. Besides the three houses near Salmon Creek in Pultneyville, the Hallet and Cuyler houses owned by distinguished Pultneyville families were also underground stations—the end of the slaves' long and arduous journey to freedom.

This night the slaves were to find haven in the salt-box house on lot 3. As they approached the back of the house, the door opened. The leader entered, the others followed. They crossed the room to the stairs in the right-hand corner. A few steps took them to a right-angle turn, and then more steps carried them up to the second floor. Another right turn brought them to a bedroom with a ladder leading to a small trap door in the ceiling approximately 15 inches wide and 27 inches long. Each slave mounted the rungs as he was told. As the last one placed his foot on the rung, he turned to the guide; and no longer able to contain himself, he said, as he slowly shook his head, "Judge—there's sumpthin' awful wrong about that branch water out there." The Negro, excitedly told the local Justice about the bark strip that seemed to float both ways.

The Justice looked at him for a moment and then said evenly, "Yes, 'tis a strange thing. Seems to be no accounting for it. Salmon Creek sometimes just seems to flow in both directions. Don't ask me why. We're close to where it empties into the lake. Perhaps the lake has something to do with it. I really don't know."

"Judge, don't you see, that means no good to us. That going back and forth means the Sheriff's men will catch us and carry us back in chains. It's a powerful bad omen."

The Justice replied, "Don't you worry yourself. I don't know why the Creek flows both ways; but I do know that the courage which has brought you this far, with God's help, will take you to freedom."

The Negro seemed to get more assurance out of the Judge's manner and expression than out of the words he used. For a moment longer, the Negro studied the Judge, tried a smile and then climbed the ladder to the attic. The crawl space under the eaves above the rooms was just that. The slaves had just enough space to slip in and lie down. They stretched their tired bodies across the rafters and fell asleep. The heat of the day was still in the attic, but already the cool lake night air coming through the dwarf windows in the front had begun to cool and freshen it. In this underground station when space permitted, they kept the slaves in the attic by night when it tended to be cool there, and in the cellar during the day for the same reason.

Before daybreak that particular morning, a knock on the trap door awakened the men. As the one farthest to the front of the house opened his eyes, he noticed the early morning light filtering in through the tiny windows. From the window lights, he saw the lake stretching east and west and north disappearing in the distance. Beyond that horizon line lay freedom. Two wharves stretched out into the lake. They bent toward each other like arms, almost enclosing a part of the water and forming an artificial harbor. It was as if Pultneyville had embraced the lake. Several white-sailed schooners rolled at anchor. The steamer *Ontario* was tying up at the dock. The western wharf, just east of the mouth of Salmon Creek, had several warehouses. The dock itself was large enough for a yoke of oxen to turn around.

Many a captain and his boat called Pultneyville home port. Perhaps most famous of all was Captain Horatio Nelson Throop, a descendant of Connecticut Yankees, builder of boats, lake captain extraordinary; and it's said, the first child to be born in Pultneyville. His was the substantial cobblestone house on Lot 1. It was one of the three houses on Washington Avenue that backed onto the creek. A cobblestone house fitted the Captain. The stone had been washed smooth and dredged up out of his beloved Ontario. What better material for building a lake captain's home than the stuff the lake water helped to fashion? His sailing days were mostly over now; but on rare and important occasions, he took command again, along with his faithful friend Jeppa, his beloved Italian greyhound. This day and this night was such a time for Captain Throop.

As the slave looked out of the harbor from the attic, lost in the promise of it all, he wondered if that steamer, then snug at the wharf, might be his boat to freedom. Already he had mused too long. A tug on his leg and a whispered word started him crawling backwards toward the trap door. One by one, the Negroes retraced their steps of the night before to the first-floor room where they had originally entered. In the corner, diagonally opposite the stair well, a long narrow trap door approximately 6 feet by

4 feet was lifted up. One by one, the men dropped through the trap door to the cellar below. The trap shut, and normal household duties resumed.

Soon the village was awake and up and doing. Farmers' wagons, having started out the night before, moved out to the dock to unload apples, peaches, grapes, grains—all of the produce of the rich hinterland farms. In the Sessions House, diagonally across the street from the underground station, official looking men walked through its doors to start their daily work. The local Justice of the Peace entered. Only a few knew that he had already done a worthy night's work. There were also Federal men entering the Sessions House—the Customs men charged with the duty to enforce the Federal laws—the Fugitive Slave Act, among others.

Also that day, the Pultneyville natives would see a few strangers walking along Washington Avenue. They were the Sheriff's men from the South—slave owners' agents looking for run-away slaves. These were the men the underground tried to avoid. They were the hunters; the Negroes the hunted—men on both sides from the North and from the South trying to outwit each other. For each the gain was worth the effort.

Inside and outside the salt-box house and the other beautiful homes along Washington Avenue, chore work went on as usual. Villagers along the street passed the time of day with farmers. Those who had unloaded had more time to chat. Those just pulling into the wharves had time only for a quick "hello."

In the cellar of the small frame house with only wisps of light coming in, the slaves could hear the chatter of voices on the village streets, the rumble of oxen carts and the many footsteps of household activities on the floor above. Several times during the day, a shaft of light would force them to huddle against the stone wall in front of the cellar. Assured that it was food being brought to them, they would move back toward the trap door to get it. For the villagers, the day passed fast, filled with the hundreds of tasks to keep life going. Outwardly, it was just like any other day. For some, however, huddled in dark places, it could be the last day of slavery.

Night came. The official men left the Sessions House; the Customs men went down to the dock to check Captain Throop's passenger lists and cargo. The Sheriff's men hung menacingly about the wharf.

At the salt-box house, the Judge—leader of the night before—opened the trap door, offering the men a hand to pull them up. From the front windows, the ladies of the household watched for the signal from Captain Throop's steamer. Standing on the bridge of the *Ontario*, Captain Throop, an expert banjo player, who had learned how to play from the Negroes he had carried to freedom, started plunking out Southern tunes. This drew the Southerners to the far end of the wharf. Playing the numbers they called out, the Captain completely diverted their attention, while the Judge, seeing the signal, led his men quickly out of the house, across the street through the cellar of the warehouse and into the woodpiles that extended from one end of the wharf to the other. To the casual observer, this steamer fuel seemed to have been piled in a haphazard way; but to Captain Throop, the Judge, and the other members of the underground, it formed an intricate passageway that led from the warehouse at the beginning of the wharf to the very end of the dock where the *Ontario* was docked. Swiftly, the fugitives moved through the woodpile. The Judge, meanwhile, walked in full sight along the edge of the dock to where the steamer *Ontario* was snubbed. As the Judge approached, the Captain hallooed to him; and the Southern men passed their greetings. The Judge, looking up at Captain Throop, said,

"Captain Throop, what do you carry?"

To this, the Captain replied, "My boat runs for passengers."

The Judge replied, "Have you sufficient fuel for the voyage?"

These words were the code to indicate that Negroes were in the woodpile. The Judge, turning to the Sheriff's men, indicated a good card game was in the offing and would they like to come along. With this and with the assurance from the Captain that no slaves were aboard, the Judge led the Sheriff's men back along the wharf to the shore. Quickly the Negroes moved from the woodpile, down the plank and into the hold of the vessel. On the bridge above, Captain Throop stroked Jeppa, who rested his head on his paws on the railing. With the last man aboard, the Captain yelled through his speaking horn, "Cast off." As the boat left the pier, Throop smiled. The "Nigger in the woodpile" trick had worked again. Below deck one Negro prayerfully said, "Oh Lord! I'm free! That little boat that brought me here is going back to get my brothers—back and forth, Oh Lord! Back and forth to freedom. Its God's waters that flows both ways to get us and bring us to freedom."

Fanciful and imaginative, you say. Well, perhaps, but of such stories are folk tales made. If you go to Pultneyville today, they say you can still see the creek that sometimes flows in both directions. You can still see the salt-box house with the brick front addition. Inside, the trap doors are still there. (I know, I saw them.) The Lawrence and Throop houses live in quiet dignity; and in the window of Captain Throop's cobblestone house, a lifelike Jeppa, 85 years dead, still looks out of the window as though waiting for his master to return. On a stone cairn near Salmon

Creek and the old wharf, the names of the captains and their boats that called Pultneyville their home port are forever inscribed. And in the homes that grace the lovely streets, gracious and dignified ladies remember these stories and the stories of other people now long dead. In their memories, the life of the past of Pultneyville still lives; and proud they are that "Nigger in the woodpile" meant freedom for so many Negroes.

TO A POOR OLD BUM

I'm going, I'm going, for I know my time has come!
And to the workhouse I must go, a poor old bum.
As a free-lunch destroyer, I'm the terror of the route,
I can wrastle with the sausage or a plate of sauerkraut
And when I get a plate of beans, oh, don't I make them
hum!
They're such a solid comfort to a poor old bum.

From Prof. J. V. Denney, Head of the English Department, Ohio State University

BURNT BREAD AND BROOM HANDLES

Belching smoke, cinders, and fire, the west-bound freight slowed as it approached the outer railyards of Buffalo. In a few minutes, the lumbering train would grind to a stop with much hissing, clanging and screeching. The stopping of a train always reminded Joe of the last convulsive gasp of some huge thing dying. For Joe, this would be the last time he would have to listen to the cacophony of a freight train for awhile.

Joe had been riding the rails from New York City, spending the last stretch of the journey from Batavia to Buffalo atop a boxcar the better to see the country near the lake. As the train pulled in the yard near the soot-covered

) 124 (

red brick passenger station on Exchange Street, he lowered himself down the steel ladder on the north side of the car. Facing west with a firm left hand on the grabstep and his left foot on the steel step just above the ground, he swung back and using his right hand as a sort of balance, stepped from the train. As his foot touched the cinders, he ran forward a few steps to keep from pitching forward on his face. Looking about quickly to see if there were any rail police around, he dashed across the railyard and out onto Exchange Street.

As he walked west on Exchange Street, he looked over at the train. It now seemed to have relaxed from its stopping spasm and only the steady throbbing of the locomotive could be heard. In the early morning, Exchange Street was quiet. It seemed to be sleeping off its last night's drunk. The sound of the engine idling on the rail siding added the illusion of heavy breathing. An early morning haze seemed to accentuate the stillness of inactivity. Not a soul was stirring. The lonely click of Joe's heels on the cobblestone echoed against the walls of the buildings which lined Exchange Street opposite the yard.

If his canawler friend at Coenties Slip in New York had informed him correctly, he would soon be crossing Main Street opposite which he would spot the twin pumps. Beyond this would be the bridge over the Erie Canal which would take him into the Buffalo waterfront district. As he crossed the bridge, he thought of the thousands who had walked down Commercial and Canal Streets on their way to the Old Northwest.

While still a busy and important place, the waterfront's future was in its past. Progress had passed it by. Having crossed the bridge over the canal, Joe now turned right off Commercial Street onto Canal Street, once named Cross and later to be named Dante Place. It was like a still picture, nothing moved. In almost all of the alleys, Joe could see drunks sleeping off their whiskey stupor; hair disheveled, clothes dirty and their bodies reeking with the sour smell of cheap liquor. A few buildings away from Commercial Street, Joe turned left down Maiden Lane toward the harbor. Perhaps, he thought idly, I might get a job as a scooper.

The closer Joe walked toward the harbor, the thicker the haze became. The sun, having only started its climb, had not succeeded in dispelling it yet. He sat down on what looked to be some comfortably padded freight and promptly fell fast asleep. A moment later, or so it seemed, Joe was awakened by a voice saying, "Come on buddy, move it."

"O.K.," said Joe, "I'm going." He looked at the fellow for a second and then added, "Don't need an extra hand, do you?"

"Nope," said the hustler, "got too many as 'tis."

With that, Joe started back toward the canal. This time he walked along Commercial Street which edged on the Commercial Slip. In what to him had seemed like only a few minutes, the area had been completely transformed. Where there had been only quiet before, there was now the hustle and bustle of noisy confusion. It seemed to Joe almost as if the sailors, canawlers, dock-hands, deck-hands, scoopers, clerks, commission merchants, immigrants and waterfront rats in general, had formed out of nothingness.

The saloons had already opened their doors in order to catch the early morning trade. There were always those who needed a "starter" and those who had to put out the roaring fires which they had kindled the night before. As Joe pushed through the swinging doors of a saloon, at the corner of Commercial and Canal Streets, such a character had just downed a shot in one sweeping gesture and with perfect synchronization followed it with a water chaser. He grimaced like one in great pain and said, "God, that's good. I always say ya have to fight fire with fire."

Joe stepped up to the bar. "A shot, please."

As the barkeeper turned to get it, Joe looked about the room. Over in the corner where just a sprig of light played on a table, someone sat writing. Joe studied his face. He had a feeling he had seen it somewhere before. He looked hard. Then the thought came to him. No, it couldn't be, Jack had left for the coast over a month ago.

Joe turned his attention back to his drink, smelled it for a moment, and then flipped it up to his mouth. As he set the glass down with one hand, he took a swig of water with the other. Turning to the bartender, he asked him who the lone customer was over at the table in the corner.

"Dunno where he came from," said the barkeep, "but he asked me when the next west-bound freight was leaving and I told him that one had arrived from the East early this morning and would be pulling out in about an hour. I reckon he's fixin' to skip along."

While the bartender talked, Joe continued to study the man's face closely. It couldn't be, he thought to himself, but by God, it was. It was his old pal Jack. Joe quickly walked over to the table.

"Why, you silver-plated bum," Joe yelled, "what in hell are you doing in Buffalo? I thought by now you'd be in Frisco."

The person at the table dropped his pencil, looked up at Joe and a broad warm smile broke across his face.

"Joe, you rod-riding son-of-a-rail, it's good to see you. Watcha doing here?" Jack said as he stood up from the table and grabbed Joe's hand.

"No fair, Jack. I asked you first. Let's have it. What happened? You didn't get a job and go respectable on me, did you?"

"Yes, and no, Joe."

"You mean you did get a job? Who'd ever hire the likes of you?"

"Now look here Joe, I'm not so bad when you get to know me. I can think of a number of people who might hire me. As a matter of fact, a number of people did hire me."

Joe looked steadily at his friend for a moment and in mock disbelief said, "Who?"

"Erie County," replied Jack with a straight face.

"Erie County?" said Joe, no longer faking his disbelief. "What do ya mean, Erie County?"

"I mean," Jack insisted, "Erie County hired me."

"Now wait a minute, Jack, what in hell have you got that Erie County could possibly want?"

"Me, I guess," Jack said, trying to keep a straight face.

"All right, all right, Jack. I'll admit I was never quite as sharp as you and now you got me tied for sure. Come clean. What really happened?"

"Well I'll tell you, Joe, I have just spent thirty days as the guest of the Erie County jail."

"No," said Joe, "you can't really mean that. I know you're capable of a great many things. I never thought you would stoop to stealing. Not one who can talk people out of money the way you can."

"Truth is, Joe, just the opposite happened. I was picked up at the Falls on a vagrancy charge and tossed into the Erie County jail with all the trash and garbage of the Buffalo waterfront."

"Well I certainly am surprised," Joe said, "I always thought you'd make your own way. Never thought you would stoop to having the Government take care of you. How does it feel to have had a well-fed and slept vacation?"

Whatever humor had been in Jack's face now melted away and in its place an expression of deep revulsion appeared.

"Joe, believe me, there has been no humor in my experience of the last month. This so-called jail where they housed me for thirty days is located on the canal. The prisoners are made to carry huge stay-bolts, railroad ties, stone and other heavy freight boated in on the canal. They kept us at it for eighteen hours a day. The work was hard, too hard considering the prison diet. Bread and water, that was all that was given us. Once a week we were supposed to get meat, but this meat did not always get around, and since all the nutriment had been boiled out of it in the making of soup, it didn't matter whether we got a taste of it once a week or not.

"Furthermore, there was one vital defect in the bread and water diet. While we got plenty of water, we did not get enough bread. A ration of bread was about the size of one's fist and three rations a day were given to each prisoner. There was one thing I must say, about the water— it was hot. In the morning it was coffee, at noon it was dignified as soup, and at night it masqueraded as 'tea.' But it was the same old water all the time. The prisoners called it water bewitched. In the morning it was black water, the color being due to boiling it with burnt bread crust. At noon it was served minus the color, with salt and a drop of grease added. At night it was served with a purplish-auburn hue that defied all speculation; it was darn poor tea but it was dandy hot water."

Joe laughed and said, "What are you complaining about? Look what it's done for your waistline."

"Joe, perhaps I can make light of the food situation, but believe me, there is nothing, absolutely nothing to mitigate the utter brutality prisoners are forced to endure in the Erie County penitentiary. Joe, if I had not seen it with my own eyes, I would never have believed that such conditions existed in America in this year of civilization 1890. That prison was a living hell. The treatment of prisoners was not only unprintable, it was unthinkable. Because of insufficient personnel, certain inmates are made trustees. They are called hall-men. I suppose considering the nature of the waterfront brutes they picked up, it was impossible to rule by kindness. Yet some humanity could have been employed. Their rule was to hit a man as soon as he opened his mouth—hit him hard, hit him with anything. A broom handle, end on in the face, had a very sobering effect. I remember a young mulatto about twenty who got the insane idea into his head that he should stand for his rights. Eight hall-men took the conceit out of him in just about a minute and a half—for that was the length of time required to travel along his gallery to the end and down five flights of steel stairs. He traveled the whole distance on every portion of his anatomy except his feet, and the eight hall-men were not idle. The mulatto struck the pavement where I was standing watching it all. He regained his feet and stood upright for a moment. In that moment he threw his arms wide apart and emitted an awful scream of terror and pain and heartbreak. At the same instant, as in a transformation scene, the shreds of his stout prison clothes fell from him, leaving him wholly naked and streaming blood from every portion of the surface of his body. Then he collapsed in a heap, unconscious. He had learned his lesson, and every convict within those walls who heard him scream had learned a lesson. So had I learned mine. It is not a nice thing to see a man's heart broken in a minute and a half."

Jack looked over at Joe for a fleeting second. Joe had been hanging on his every word. There was a look of horror on his face.

Then slowly Joe said, "Jack, there are no brute animals as inhuman as human beings. I have never had such a deep feeling of revulsion as I had when you told that story. But I could not help also thinking that you have a great gift for story-telling. You seem to be able to make the things which you see and experience live again for others through your words."

"Joe, I always felt that I had some ability along that line. That's why I was writing when you interrupted me a few minutes ago. I did not want to lose the story I just told you and you know, Joe, I would like nothing better than to see a printed title on a book one day with the name Jack—Jack London—after it."

"Well, Joe, my train leaves in a few minutes. After what I've just told you, you don't want to stay around this town, do you?"

Joe took a letter out of his pocket, looked at it for a moment and then tore it up. "You're right, Jack, let's hit the road."

Jack turned with this to Joe and after a few seconds said, "You know, Joe, maybe that's what I'll call this book, *The Road*, by Jack London."[1]

---

[1] The description of conditions in the Erie County jail quoted directly from Jack London's writings.

AS CROOKED AS THE CRICK

Captain Sam lifted his fishing pole just a mite, considered the water expertly for a moment and then dropped his line a smidge to the left of his original spot. Sitting on the next snubbing post, watching his Grampa's every move, was Jerry. He knew whatever his grandfather did was the right thing to do whether it was just plain livin' or just plain fishin'. In fact, if there was anything about fishing Captain Sam didn't know, Jerry was certain the fish didn't know either. Gramp had told him so many times. "I know all there is to know about the Great Lakes. Yes, boy! and all about all the rivers and the cricks that run into them. I should know all about them. I've sailed these inland seas for fifty years as man and boy." Always the ideas and words remained the same. The number of years, however, had a way of growing larger with each telling.

Mimicking his Gramp, Jerry himself now lifted his pole, scanned the water momentarily and then placed it back a little bit to his left. Two water circles grew out from the spot where the lines had been reset. They soon overlapped. As Gramp watched them intertwine, they seemed to be a sort of symbol of the bond which linked him to his grandson.

For awhile both sat quietly in fisherman's contentment, completely and perfectly in tune with the universe. Then, just as Gramp had cut the satin smoothness of the water when he changed fishing positions, Jerry now decided it was about time to reset the conversation line. He broke into the silence abruptly. "Seems to me, Gramp, that if you outsmarted those blacklegged gamblers who used to fleece the people in the Canal Street saloons on the Buffalo waterfront, they couldn't have been very crooked." A little smile pushed up the edges of Jerry's mouth and he added, "Unless, of course, you were as crooked as they were."

"Now see here, young fellow, your hull is getting a mite too big for the size of your sail. I'm telling you and I know. Those blacklegged gamblers along Canal Street were the crookedest crooks on the lake. Why, Jerry, they were as crooked as this crick. And believe me, boy, this is just about the crookedest crick on the lake. I know, cause I sailed up them all and, though I never scratched a keel board in any of 'em, I came closest to staving in my port belly right here on this misshapen crick. Believe me, Jerry, many a pilot did just that. No doubt of it, lad, Buffalo Crick is as crooked as a snake."

Captain Sam paused a moment so the comparison would register on Jerry. Then looking directly at him and measuring each word as if he expected opposition, he said, "Fact is, son, it's as crooked as a snake because an oversized snake made it that way." Jerry had heard many of Gramp's stories and had trained himself not to show too much surprise at what he said. This, however, seemed to be going a bit too far, even for Gramp. "Now wait a minute, Gramp," said Jerry, "that's not what they tell us at school."

"Can't help what they tell you at school," snapped Gramp, "the Indians told me why Buffalo Crick is so crooked and what's good enough for the Indians ought to be good enough for the likes of you and those old maid schoolmarms. I reckon my Indian friends stretch back a lot more years than those book readin', chalk scratchin' teachers of yours. You know, Jerry, I believe you're catchin' too much wind in your canvas. Boy, my advice to you is to trim your sails sharply when those schoolmarms start blowing."

Jerry started to smile but then quickly checked himself because he didn't want his Gramp to see him.

"Okay, son, now do you want to go on believing what those landlubbing teachers tell you or do you really want to find out how Buffalo Crick came to be the crookedest crick on the lakes?"

Jerry knew he didn't have to say anything because Gramp would spin his tale anyhow. So he only smiled at Gramp, settled back into a comfortable position on the snubbing post and wondered whether he had heard this one.

"Well, sir," Gramp began, "a long time ago, long before the white man came to this crick, in fact long before the white man had discovered America, yes, even before the Indians had lived on this bank, Buffalo Crick flowed straight as an arrow and clear as moonlight. Came out of the hills southeast of here and made a plumb line for the mouth over yonder, the way any sensibly minded crick ought to do.

"At this time an Indian tribe lived on the banks of Cayuga Crick which empties into the Niagara River just above the Falls. Today the settlement is called LaSalle. In those days, the Indians called it Ga-U-Gwa, which the white man translated into Cayuga. In that village lived the prettiest young Indian maiden for miles around. Her whole life had been filled with happiness until one day she learned that her mother and father had promised her in marriage to a miserable old man. 'Cordin' to the customs of her people, only death could save her from such a marriage. In this case she preferred death.

"So at sunup one morning, she pushed her bark canoe out of Cayuga Crick and into Niagara River. Pointing the bow northward, the current soon caught hold of the canoe and carried it swiftly into the upper rapids above the Falls. Quietly she dropped the paddles, calmly folded her hands and with serene contentment waited to be swept over the cataract to her death. In a few moments the canoe shot over the brink and plunged toward the bottom of the gorge where the waters boiled up from the huge jagged rocks. In those few moments, a miracle occurred.

"When the canoe crashed on the rocks, the Indian girl was not in it. The great God of Thunder, who lived in the Cave of the Winds behind the Falls, had watched the girl floating in her canoe toward the edge of the cataract. Such had been the godlike serenity on her beautiful face and her calm acceptance of fate that Heno, the God of Thunder, had been moved to save her. Quickly as her canoe caromed through the turbulent waters of the upper rapids and over the Horseshoe Falls, he reached out a blanket of silver mist and caught her in it. He then carried her uninjured behind the wall of falling water. There he laid her on a bed of soft mist and told one of his assistants to care for her. No sooner did Heno's helper see her than he fell deeply in love with her. When she awakened, she looked up into his face and knew that this was the Prince she had always dreamed about. He gathered her up into his arms and kissed her. Soon after, Heno married the happy pair.

"Now it so happened that for several years before this happened, the people of Ca-U-Gwa suffered each year from a dreadful pestilence which took a great toll of lives. Nothing they did seemed to prevent or lessen the disease. In the course of time, Heno grew quite fond of the Indian girl he had saved and resolved to tell her the cause and cure of the plague which brought wholesale death to her people. At the year's end, he told her the cause of the pestilence. He then gave her permission to return to her people and save them.

"After she had been safely delivered back to her people, the Indian girl told them the story of her rescue by Heno, the God of Thunder. She also told them that a monster serpent dwelt in the ground beneath the village. Each year he feasted on the dead bodies buried conveniently by the side of the village. To make sure he had enough to eat at his annual feast, the serpent poisoned the waters of the Cayuga Crick and Niagara River. Since the Indians at this time did not know how to get water out of the ground, they depended entirely on the crick and the river for their drinking water. So the Indian girl told her people they would have to leave the village and live on the banks of Buffalo Crick.

"Not long after, the serpent, unable to find enough bodies for his feast, pushed his head above the ground and discovered the village deserted. Enraged, he immediately picked up the scent, plunged madly into the Niagara River and swam southward toward the Lake. At Buffalo Crick, he spotted the new village and prepared to devour the people. Heno, who was watching everything from a mist cloud above the Falls, opened the heavens and discharged his most terrible thunderbolts, one of which wounded the snake severely. In his agony, the snake thrashed madly from one side of the crick to the other. Each desperate lunge pushed back the bank and twisted the crick all out of shape. At one point the monster almost broke through into the open water of the lake. Meanwhile, Heno kept hurling one thunderbolt after another at the huge writhing body. As the lightning bolts took effect, the thrashing and turning became less and less strenuous. Eventually, the body of the serpent lay still, cradled in the new bed of the crick. The serpent was dead. The people were free. But the crick would never be the same. To reach the lake, the crick now took five miles to cover what it had formerly covered in two. In those last five miles, the crick now flowed north, south, east and points between before it finally decided to flow west into the lake.

"Yes, Jerry, my boy, Buffalo Crick is the crookedest crick on the lakes—crooked as a snake." Jerry smiled back at his Gramp and reset his fishing line. This was one he hadn't heard.

THE GIRLS IN THE POLICE GAZETTE

Oh, the girls are in the Police Gazette
The crew are all in jail,
I'm the only living sea-cook's pet
That's left to tell the tale.

The Devil Wore a Cane and Crutch

THE DEVIL WORE A CANE AND CRUTCH

How endless the waiting seemed; even when death waited too. Grim faced men, the youthful and the old, peered across the dark water seeing nothing but blackness—that and moving shadows cast by their uneasy minds. They waited. They were the invaders. What a frightening and formidable name for peaceful farm boys from the North country of York State, from the Mohawk Valley, from villages and towns upstate and downstate, and from neighboring states. Many of them had wanted no part of this Niagara invasion. Most of all, they had wanted to get home to their farms and families.

But for them this year there would be no farming. It was October 13, 1812, the beginning of the war that would forever bear that year name. Although history had not yet decided to call it the War of 1812, American patriots referred to it as the "Second War of Independence"; some politicians bitterly denounced it as "Mr. Madison's War." Canadians fighting for their land and feeling the first glow of nationalism described it as a "War of Survival." To the militia men, however, it didn't matter much what anyone called it. It was still war. That they knew and the fact that they now stood on the American shore waiting for the signal to enter the small boats hidden beneath the thick, brambly underbrush that edged the Niagara River. They were ready to move; some even eager. Since they were here to fight, they were all for getting the fight started and over with. They, like the armies of all ages, feared the waiting more than the fighting.

Across the river lay Canada—now enemy country. Beneath the sharp Niagara escarpment lay the Queen's Town, shortened in usage to Queenston. Above it were the

Heights where the dramatic battle would take place. At Lewiston opposite, on the United States side, the army of invasion stood poised at the bottom of the escarpment. Between the two settlements the Niagara River flowed and eddied, dark and deep toward Lake Ontario. Here where the River splits the mountain, the waters of Niagara find peace after their turbulent struggle to fight their way through seven miles of narrow rock gorge. Smoothly, the water glides into the open lands, leaving behind the roaring sounds of the lower rapids bouncing against the steep stone cliffs. In fifty thousand years, according to some geologists, Niagara Falls had cut this canyon 275 feet deep at this point and at lesser heights back to the present site of the Falls. Atop this escarpment, high above the heads of the men, Niagara Falls had been born. From here, it had eaten its way back seven miles through the hard Lockport dolomite and Medina red sandstone.

At the moment, however, there was no place in their thinking or feeling for comtemplating the Falls and gorge of Niagara. The men were filled only with the gnawing emptiness of fear. They scuffed their feet against the loose stones. In front of them the invasion boats tugged nervously at their lines as if they, too, were tired of waiting.

One man alone could end the waiting. His name was General Stephen Van Rensselaer, scion of the Hudson Valley patroons. On him rested the awful decision of invasion. The demoralizing delay had been caused not by his indecision, but by the infamous treachery of a river pilot. Earlier it had been discovered that the pilot in charge of the crossing had apparently turned traitor, cut the invasion boats loose and presumably escaped to Canada. Questions of doubt, that had not entered Van Rensselaer's mind originally, now shook his confidence. How much did the Canadians know now about his plans? Only with surprise could the Americans hope for a gambler's chance of success. Otherwise, the operation, conceived in complete violation of almost all accepted military principles, could prove tragically disastrous. Eventually, however, Van Rensselaer in his own conscience resolved his fears and decided to go ahead according to plan. Fortunately, the General had in the meantime bolstered his confidence by securing the valuable services of the loyal Cooke brothers, Lemuel and Lothrop of Lewiston.

A long decade before, these two pioneers had built the first log cabin in Lewiston not far from the present invasion encampment. Later, while his brother Lemuel bought land east of the village of Lewiston, Lothrop, hearing of cheaper land across the river, bought a section of it in Canada. The War found him in enemy territory. Refusing to swear allegiance to the English King, Lothrop and his family escaped forty miles across the Lake and up the river to Lewiston. Not many people knew the river and the land that held it better than the Cookes. Few, if any, loved it more. The General knew he could depend on the Cooke brothers.

With the boats ready, the men anxious, and the pilots on hand, the General gave the signal. In the darkness, the men quietly entered the boats. The first into the river carried the Cookes and Colonel Solomon Van Rensselaer, kin of the General, and in charge of the beachhead operation.

To assault and dislodge a determined enemy securely entrenched atop a 275 foot cliff required courage and agility. Rather than risk a deadly frontal attack, Van Rensselaer planned a flanking movement that followed the fisherman's path to Queenston Heights. Slowly, the pilots picked their way by sound and feel across the river. They took fifteen minutes before they touched land. At the very instant Colonel Van Rensselaer stepped ashore a volley of shots cut him down. He was struck four times. Lothrop tried to grab him and get him into the boat. As he did so, his foot slipped on a stone and he fell against a jagged rock which tore a deep wound in the fleshy part of his leg. Still he managed to pull the colonel into the boat. Soon Lothrop had him safely back on the American side.

Giving no thought to his own wound, Cooke continued ferrying men across the river as fast as he could make the round trip. Despite the heavy Canadian fire, the Americans succeeded in establishing a beachhead. They fought their way up the path to the Canadian entrenchment on the heights.

With the heights secured, the General called for reinforcements to meet the anticipated counter-attack. On his next trip back, Lothrop carried the order to an American Major in charge of the second wave. Incredibly, at the moment of apparent victory, the Major refused to order his men across. Abandoned on top of the escarpment, the American men, faced with armies under Brock, McDonnell and Sheaffe, surrendered. Half a thousand Americans were taken. The Battle of Queenston Heights was over. Born ignominiously in treachery, it ended in treachery. America's first invasion attempt had failed.

Many battles later, the war ended. For most, memories of the river crossing dimmed. Lothrop had cause not to forget the tragic morning of battle. Intent on his ferrying work that morning, Lothrop Cooke had neglected to have his wound treated. Finally in exhaustion he turned for medical attention. It was too late. Infection had set in deeply. Only amputation could save his life. With several stiff swigs of whiskey to ease the pain, and a lead ball between his teeth to bite on, he watched the medics saw off his leg. Lothrop lived through the ordeal, but it was months before the shock and weakness left him.

Over the years following the war and operation his tall, powerful, six-foot figure became familiar and respected on the Niagara Frontier as he moved about on a leg, a cane, and a crutch. When the state separated the counties of Erie and Niagara in 1821, Governor DeWitt Clinton appointed Lothrop Cooke sheriff of Niagara County. He served in that official capacity and later as Deputy Sheriff. Peaceful citizens loved, and lawbreakers feared, "Ole Cane and Crutch." He soon came to personify law and order. Day by day Cooke performed the duties of his office.

One of those days he experienced a delicious and ironic twist of history that happens only infrequently in a man's lifetime. For sometime, a despicable character had been abusing his neighbors by poisoning their horses and oxen. With a warrant in hand, Lothrop set out to bring him in. He found his man hoeing in his field close to the fence where the road ran. Riding up close to him, Cooke engaged him in idle but disarming conversation. He knew his man always carried a pistol and never hesitated to use it.

After some minutes of small talk, Cooke, in a voice of surprise and a gesture of direction, exclaimed, "What is that vessel doing so near shore? She will go aground." The farmer looked up quickly. As he did, Cooke leaped from his horse, pushed the man to the ground, drew his pistol, and handcuffed him.

As they rode back, Lothrop looked at his prisoner and smiled. He had reason to be pleased. Of all the men he had ever arrested, this man deserved most to be brought to justice. He glanced down at the stump of his leg, he thought of that battle night many years ago, of the dying, and the dead. Memory sent a sharp pain through what remained of his leg; disdain dropped from the corners of his lips and hardened his face. He felt slightly nauseous as he looked again at his man. This was the man, the Major of the Militia, that October 13, 1812, who had refused to cross the river to reinforce the Americans on the heights. His cowardice in large part had cost America the battle. Cooke, indeed, had reason to be more pleased with that day's work than any other. No days were unexciting for Lothrop Cooke. It was just that some days were more exciting than others.

In the 1820's the tempo of that excitement increased

noticeably. Those years saw the coming of the Erie Canal. During the digging, an estimated two thousand laborers, mostly emigrants from Ireland, worked in and around Lockport. Being from the north and south of Ireland, their politics and religion differed. Stimulated by cheap whiskey drunk almost as freely as water (and far safer than some water) the workers, who labored hard twelve hours each day, frequently found themselves in fights in or near the shanties built along the canal bank west of the village. The natives lived in constant fear that the brawling would sometimes spill over into the village.

One day, it did. A full scale riot broke loose. Several hundred canal workers, fortified on the inside with whiskey and on the outside with sticks and stones and picks and shovels, threatened the villagers.

Cooke was called in immediately. "How many men do you need?"

"None whatever!" came the quick answer. "You have not enough citizens to make the arrests if they resist, but they will not look on a single one-legged man as a defiance."

Before the staff recovered, Cooke started out the door and on toward the edge of the village where the diggings were located. In slow rhythm, Lothrop swung his huge frame forward on his cane and crutch. Towering like a tall tree with half a trunk, his massive form swayed and moved magically and most untree-like. At a distance, as the rioters came out of the lock basin, the lone figure lumbering across the field toward them seemed grotesque and ridiculous. "A cripple sent to stop them." They shouted taunts and they belly laughed as they charged across the field, yelling like banshees and brandishing their picks and shovels. Cooke's tall powerful figure and long limbs grew taller, longer, and stronger as the distance closed. The mob began to slow its pace as it looked and wondered. To the superstitious Irish, the dishevelled hair, determined chin, set lips, and blazing eyes made the figure less a man and more a demon.

Cooke clutched the warrant in his fist. He worked his cane and crutch like instruments bent on destruction. The leader hesitated. The gang stopped. For a moment, Cooke stood thirty feet away, glancing at his adversary. At that instant he dropped his cane and crutch, swung his arms over his head in an arc and lunged forward. With three prodigious leaps on his one powerful leg, Cooke, all six-foot five of him, landed on top of the bug-eyed leader. In terror, he had stumbled and fallen as he started to run. Cooke pinned him to the ground with his leg stump. Screaming for mercy, the gang leader called out to his men, "Run, run, the devil with one leg is after me!"

Turning to the huge form over him, he cried, "I surrender, I surrender!" Cooke's face softened and he said, "Send the rioters back to work and I'll tear up the warrant."

The man looked up and said, "Sheriff, you are a brave and kind man. I will do it."

The villagers always remembered that day. Lothrop Cooke became a legend among them. And the Irish storytellers, too, with their fine sense of delightful exaggeration never forgot the day the devil came on a cane and a crutch and just one leg to chase the canal diggers back to their diggings.

Black Becomes the Bride's Ghost

BLACK BECOMES THE BRIDE'S GHOST

Slowly, as if moved by an unseen hand, the huge boulder rolls aside. Up from beneath the rock, the Indian Princess and her warrior Prince, dead these many years, arise. Once again the two ghost lovers walk hand in hand along the bank of their creek. For an hour, they walk the earth again. Then, they return to their watery grave under the rock. Again the rock moves back into place and the stream resumes its peaceful flow around it. What better testament of the immortality of true love! In Claverack, New York, in the Hudson Valley, they call this the Legend of Spook Rock of Claverack Creek. If you're a willing listener, the people thereabouts will tell you this story in a number of variations as well as many another ghost story from the haunted Valley of the Hudson. But before the stories, a word or more about ghosts in general and more particularly the Hudson Valley species.

In that valley of spring and summer green, across from the lore-filled Catskills whose peaks the summer sunsets paint a deep purple, there are those—the very young, with the inner glow of pink on their cheeks; and those—the very old, with the sky color of sun and the soil color of earth on their faces; and all those natives in between—who will tell you that the Headless Horseman still madly rides the hills and hollows along the sunrise shore of the Hudson River. In the land Washington Irving peopled with lovable lazy characters, good and ill-humored ghosts, the hapless Horseman always returns on moonful nights, especially when the frost is on the pumpkin and the wind howls down from the mountains.

To most, the ghostly ride may seem a bit overdone and rather theatrical, just a tale made up to frighten people and sell books. It did well. It did both. So thoroughly were the valley people frightened that many of them, again especially the young and the old (and all those in between) became ardent ghost believers. Remember, of all ghost believers, a scared ghost believer is the very worst—or is it the very best? With such an historic background, the Valley became a favorite haunt for ghosts. At least the believers, particularly the affrighted believers, thought so. After all, ghosts are, or rather were, people. They like to go where they are believed. Belief in ghosts among the young probably comes from an over-active imagination; among the middle-aged from an over-active thyroid; among the old, sometimes from indigestion or intoxication. Being Irish helps, too. And for some who live in the Hudson Valley, too much reading of Irving has had the same effect.

Since most ghosts live on forever, the ghost of our story, vintage 20th century, is relatively modern and young. As ghosts go, this one has not gone very far. Unlike the Legend of Sleepy Hollow, and to keep pace with the modern period, no horses dash through this story unless, of course, one wants to make a very feeble joke about the steam locomotive in the story being an iron horse.

It is also probably true that our young ghost could do with more aging. But, in this day of speed, who can wait, even for ghosts? Still, aging would help as it always does with the better ghosts. Ghosts, unlike people, are like good wine. They seem to do better with aging. In the process, they acquire more spirit and less body. This helps them to get around more quickly, more easily, and to more people. With ghosts this is quite desirable, for they like people—all kinds of people (Why else would they return?). Everything ghost writers have dug up recently in their research undertakings seems to substantiate this. But enough of this lengthy ghost lore, let's get on with the stories.

Since our ghost isn't old, it can at least be a woman, and beautiful, and a bride. As the story has it, she is all of these. What daring but frightened boys first found the haunted honeymoon house; who first told the tale to the townfolks; who learned the secret of the ghost girl and actually unravelled the meaning of the story—all these are now lost, probably forever, in the heavy haze of the Hudson. All the historic details have dissolved in that misty past where ghosts like to gather and where there are no footprints or footnotes. Only the skeleton of the story remains, and it has been rattling around for 25 years. Here it is, as I remember hearing it then, from one who claims to have been there.

According to him, it all began, as these tall telltales sometimes do, around a Boy Scout campfire in the Mid-Hudson hinterland, east of the river. This particular night was a good one for telling ghost stories. Black clouds blotted out large chunks of sky. A storm was in the making. The boys could see it, smell it, feel it coming. After a session of spinning ghost stories from all over the world, the camp counselors then started with the local genre of ghosts—the Hudson Valley variety. They ended with the sad, sad story of Spook Rock of Claverack Creek. It went something like this:

In the time before the coming of the white man, the Konosioni wore deeply the trail through the valley of the Great River that flowed to the Big Water. One day a lone Iroquois warrior happened upon an Indian maiden of a river tribe resting not far from her bark hut. He first saw her through a break in the brush as she knelt on the bank beside a quiet pool just off the main stream of the creek. She was gently scooping up handfuls of its crystal water. After drinking for a while, she continued to palm the water, letting the coolness trickle through her long, graceful fingers. Sunshine filtering through the trees sprinkled diamonds in her dark hair.

For a moment the warrior watched her face and form in the water. She was indeed a lovely creature—far the loveliest he had ever seen. As the gently agitated water stilled and smoothed itself to a mirror, her image grew even lovelier. Soundlessly he moved closer, not wishing to disturb anything. The water caught his handsome reflection with hers. At the same instant a leaf dropped into the pool, rippling the waters and blending their faces prophetically. The forest girl was startled at first, but not frightened, by the picture in the water of the man standing behind her. Slowly she turned her head to look up at him. Then with graceful dignity she rose to face him. As the changing light caught her deep dark eyes, they flashed brightly, sparkling like star fires chipped from flint. They looked at each other for a long time. They felt much. They said nothing. Here was understanding without the need for words. From that moment on, they knew they were meant for each other.

For them there were many other days to follow, filled with the happiness of young love. But in the end, their love could never be. She was the daughter of a chieftain, a Princess. He was a Prince. Their nations were enemies to the death. They knew this as surely as they knew their love from that first day. Where love should be life, their love could be only death or even worse, life without love—a living death. The Iroquois despised the tribes of the Hudson Valley as weaklings, especially the Mohicans. They had subjected them, found them useful only to pay tribute to the warriors of the Long House. Under no circumstances would they sanction such a corruption of the good blood of the Iroquois. They tabooed the marriage.

Still in love, yet still loyal to their people, the young couple knew that only death could give them what life had denied them. For the last time they walked beside their creek, then climbed the pathway that led to a rock ledge high above the stream. On the top of the cliff a huge boulder balanced precariously and delicately. It seemed held by an invisible hand. Finally by climbing carefully they made it to the very top of the huge stone. For a moment they held each other with their eyes and arms,

Then silently, they turned, looked up, and stepped off into space and eternity. At the same instant the added weight and sudden motion on the rock caused it to teeter and break loose. Small stones and shale stirred up by the moving rock rained after it, and a dust cloud followed it down the side of mountain. With a crashing, crunching roar, the boulder plunged after the lovers, crushing their bodies beneath it in the creek. In a few minutes the noise quieted, the dirt and dust settled, and the creek took a new course around the rock.

Did the lovers really take their own lives by their own wish and will? Some say not. According to their version of the story, the Indian Princess and her Prince had planned to run away, hoping in another land to find the happiness their fathers denied them. One night, she escaped from the castle when all were asleep and met her lover at an appointed place. As they neared the cliff a storm struck. They sought refuge near the rock. Then with the suddenness of anger, a blinding flash, a thunderous roar broke out of the heavens, shaking the mountain, loosening the rock and hurling the Indian lovers to their death below, and the rock after them. It landed on top of their bodies, crushing them into the bed of the creek and sealing their grave.

All this happened before the white man began recording his history of the valley. Today the creek flows as it did then. The erosion of time has changed it little; man has changed it some. But the huge rock still rests in Claverack Creek, in precisely the same spot. For all who would like to see, they can see it. For almost all, however, that is all they'll see—the rock and the creek—nothing more. For them, the deep mystery will always remain. Only a rare few have found the true secret of Spook Rock of Claverack Creek. This is the story some of them tell.

Each night at the Angelus Hour, or whenever the church bells of Claverack toll for death, a deadly quiet descends on the creek. The rock rolls over. Up from beneath it the Indian lovers arise and move once again along the bank of the creek. When the Angelus Hour has run its time, when the bells have ceased their ringing, they disappear under the rock. Then as slowly as it moved away, the rock slips back in place.

Now lest any of you Boy Scouts think you, too, might see the ghost lovers of Spook Rock, remember this: they are only for the eyes of young lovers still pure in heart, whose love is truly as undying as the love of the Indian girl and her beloved warrior.

This tale ended the storytelling for one night. One of the counselors put a period on the session by blowing his whistle. Slowly the boys arose to make their way to their tents.

As the circle broke up, one of the more adventuresome and experienced of the scouts whispered to a few of his friends that after "lights out" they sneak out of camp on a ghost hunt. But they wanted none of the love stuff of Spook Rock. They wanted ghosts without girls. As it turned out, they were to get only a part of their wish.

With the dying fire still in sight, the ghost stories fresh in mind, and the approaching storm all about them, the boys had the proper mood and atmosphere for their trip. The boy who suggested the expedition had already mentioned that he thought he knew a likely hideout for ghosts, an abandoned house across the lake on the other side of the railroad tracks. Not a boy among them could have known that they were about to uncover one of the most fantastic ghost stories of all time. They made their way across the pond and over the tracks. As if they were actually stalking a ghost, the boys crept up on the house very slowly. Finally they reached the house. In the dark it was hard to make out its shape. There was the musty smell and feel of age—actually decay—about the house. Yet it didn't seem to be too old, just very sad.

Since the windows were too high to peer in from the ground, one of the boys shinnied himself up to the sill, brushed aside the dust covered webs and dried bugs, spit on the glass, wiped it clean, and peeked in wide-eyed. The flashlight revealed nothing but an empty room. Even the boy's imagination and delicious desire to be scared couldn't conjure up anything resembling a ghost.

Then, just as he starterd to lower himself to the ground, wondering whether he was relieved or disappointed in not finding a ghost, a hideous shriek shattered the air. Terror drained his strength, loosened his grip. He fell to the ground. Frightened for the moment, the boys huddled together in a pile beneath the window, scarcely daring to breathe. Then the one on top dared to look up. He shined his light at the window. Staring down at him, through the clear spithole in the glass, was a ghost—a sheeted figure jumping up and down and waving his arms wildly at the boys. That was enough! The boys wasted no time. They untangled and took off. The ghost, his white sheet billowing out behind, flew through the door, down the steps, over the tracks and across the field after them. Almost to the boats, one of the boys took courage to look back. He was just in time to see the ghost stumble, and fall, and what was even worse for the ghost to lose his sheet. He played his flashlight on the crumpled figure, then called to his companions to stop running. The ghost turned out to be one of their companions who had given them the slip in the dark when they first circled the house.

Laughing and joking, the boys returned to their haunted house for a last look for ghosts—this time for real ghosts. In the distance, they could see and hear the approaching storm getting nearer and nearer. They knew they had very little time. At the house the boys tried the front door, but it had slammed shut when their ghostly friend bounded through in pursuit. The back door had been bolted by him as he changed to a ghost. They were locked out.

So this time, so all could see, they fixed a board across two cut stones several feet above the ground. Now they could see in the window. Look they did. Again they saw nothing, just an empty room with a stairs flat against the side. The stairs and stair wall were painted white.

Then the storm broke with such violence, it seemed the heavens would rip apart. The hard wind sucked the leaves of the trees after it as it hissed through the branches in sweeping gusts. The wind stretched out the branches and the leaves like fingers and arms eager to flay and grab the unwary. It turned over the light colored underside of the leaves. The lightning flashes reflected on the whitish green palms of the leaves and changed the trees to a kind of ghostly ashen.

Sticking close to the house, under the eaves, the boys kept out of some of the rain. The lightning cracked and the thunder rumbled back and forth against the Catskills and the Taconic-Berkshires, rolling down the valley. On the roof and the side opposite the boys, the rain beat an ominous staccato. The boys wondered whether to break in where it was dry or to try to make it back to camp. Then a flash of light and a sound like thunder, only closer and steadier, stopped them still. And all at once they saw it in the room. They were stunned and stone silent. This was it! Whatever it was. This was it! There was no laugh in the boys now. This was not one of them playing ghost. This was the real thing! The boys stood stiff with fear. They stared unbelieving in a kind of trauma. The stair end of the room was filled with a flood of light. Then, forming out of nothing at the head of the stairs stood a beautiful girl with a bouquet in her arms, a veil over her face, and a flowing dress. It was certainly a bridal gown, but it was black. In one flowing motion, almost as she formed, she floated down the stairs moving, yet not seeming to walk—there in form, yet transparent. Near the bottom of the stairs, she dissolved into the nothingness from which she came. The light passed by and faded. The darkness, now deeper, enveloped the room. A bolt of lightning crackled across the sky. It painted grotesque shadows of dancing trees on the walls and stairs. At almost the same time with the sound of thunder that follows a bolt of lightning, a train rushed down the tracks near the house and disappeared in the distance, blending its mournful sound with the wind and the rain.

Not a word was spoken. None had to be spoken. The boys needed all their breath for running. Where there had been no motion, now there was all motion. Run they did, pell mell for the pond. This time no one looked back. They made it back across the water much faster than they had made it over.

At camp, all were asleep. But for these boys there was no sleep that night. They lay tense, tight, excited, silent. How good it felt to be dry and warm and safe under the covers. The bunks never felt better. Next morning, the camp buzzed with the incredible story; more exactly, stories, for each telling by each boy brought more embellishments. As much as they didn't want the counselors to know, the story was too good to keep from their friends. By nightfall, everyone knew at least one variation of the "Phantom Bride" story, including, unfortunately, the counselors. They, of course, treated the whole episode with amused cynicism except for their discipline of the boys for being A.W.O.L. after "lights out." The ghost hunters were confined to camp. It did not matter much to them, however, because to their bunk buddies they were heroes.

At chow time, the counselors tried to be casual about the ghost story. They covered up their curiosity by making fun of the "kids" story. Finally one dared to say what they were all thinking.

"Well, I don't know about you guys, but I'd like to have a look at that house after we get the kids bedded down."

No vote needed to be taken. This was what they all wanted to say and do. That night, those counselors who could be spared from the night operations at camp, started off for the haunted house. The sky was cloudless, filled with pinholes of light. The full moon had clear shining. They had no trouble finding the house. Even with the moon shadows playing on it, however, it did not look ghostly.

The doors were still locked. The windows were weather wedged. As their flashlights washed away the darkness, they could see nothing unusual about the empty room. Like the boys the night before, they noted the stairs and stair wall had been painted white; the rest of the walls had been papered.

They waited. Nothing happened. Off in the distance they heard the sound of an approaching train. As it grew closer, the sound grew louder. Then just about the time they would have turned their heads to watch the train go by, one said,

"Look!" and pointed inside the room. Light flooded the stair case. Then they saw it. Just as the boys had seen it, they were seeing it and not believing it. The figure of a woman formed at the head of the stairs, moved footlessly down the stairs, melting into the darkness as the light moved away, leaving the room and the counselors to the night. At the same time, the train curved by the house and rushed into the night, too.

The ghost had not been imagination. If there be ghosts, this was one of them. No one doubted that. There must be an explanation, but night time was no time for finding out. The counselors had not been so much frightened as mystified. They were happy, however, when one of their number suggested going back to camp. Tomorrow they would return during daytime. There is always more courage in daylight.

Early the next morning they were back. This time, inside the house. They examined the house upstairs and downstairs. Nothing! Then suddenly one shouted, "Look, I think I've found something!" There in the wall was an opening much larger than a peephole, but smaller than a porthole. The glass that covered it looked like a lens. There between the lens-like glass, they found their ghost—a picture of the bride. As a light played on the glass on the outside, the picture was projected on the stair wall opposite. The light obviously came from the train.

But why all this? Investigation later revealed a strange story. A man had once brought his bride to this house. A few weeks later a tragic thing happened. Crossing the tracks near the house one night, she fell. The train bore down on her, killing her instantly.

In his melancholia, the husband built the lens-like window and put his wife's bridal picture in it. Each night when the head light of the train flashed against the window lens, it played the picture on the opposite wall. As the train followed its curve around the house, the light moved away causing the image to descend the stairs. The train that had taken his loved one away, brought her back each night.

Though centuries and civilizations separated the ghost story of the Indian lovers and the modern lovers, the themes were exactly the same—the immortality of true love. May it ever be thus!

But why, in the modern theme, you ask, did the bride wear black? Well, picture prints are opaque; negatives transparent. Since only transparencies project, the negative and not the positive had to be used. In such cases, white is black and black is white. Come to think of it, perhaps this is the way it is in the ghost world, too. Things are not what they seem. Often they are just the opposite.

There may be even more to it than that. If at weddings, for purity and the promise of life, white becomes the bride, then for death, it follows that black becomes the bride's ghost.

So be it for this story. So be it here. So be it.

THE GHOST OF LOCK HERKIMER

Wherever the Irish have made their home, loveable little leprechauns and garrulous gangling ghosts have joined them. When the Irish moved from the Isle, they brought Irish spirits, ethereal as well as liquid with them. Disbelievers over the years have, of course, come to doubt the strange and wonderful Irish world of crying banshees and wispy ectoplasm, but never, God bless them, have the Irish been disbelievers. It's all very simple. They believe because they've seen. And they've seen because they have the "power." Anyone ought to be able to understand that without too much trouble.

When the Irish came to the new world to help dig the Erie Canal, they naturally brought the light-footed inhabitants of the nether region with them because they knew the little men would come anyway. As they dug the Canal, as they piled stone upon stone for the lock walls and scooped out mud from the ditch for berm bank and towpath, they built and buried their pixies into the Canal with loving care. Along with the Irish imagination, York State soil proved rich for such a planting. The ghosts of Erin Isle had found a snug home on the Erie Canal. "Bogs is bogs," they used to say to those who could understand ghost language.

Only the Irish diggers knew exactly where their invisible friends were buried. And only Paddys knew how to get them out and at what hours they would come out without asking or help. Under certain auguries (and especially for non-believers) the Irish talked rather freely about their non-terrestrial friends. Much of the Erie Canal folklore therefore has grown up around the Irish.

Unfortunately, your Irish friends today will probably not be much help in introducing you to too many (if any) of these Canal ghosts. Most of the modern Irish seem to have lost the "gift." Distance in miles and years in time from the "ould sod" have decreased the power of the "power." Some have, alas, listened too long to the disbelievers of the new world. Those who still know of such things claim that the Canal ghosts are getting restless. Sealed tomb-like for long years in stone and dirt with no exercise has not, to say the least, kept them in the best of spirits.

The present anemic ghost "power" would have been a disgrace in the old days. In the Grand Years of the Grand Canal—(the "Old Ditch" as well as the Improved)—the "Grand" Irish had the power in full amperage. There were giants in those days, to coin a phrase. Among them a driver boy. Nothing then, and it must be admitted today, is more Irish than an O'Brien, unless, of course, it is an Erie Canal Irishman named O'Brien. John O'Brien was such a man; he had the "power." He knew all about ghosts—canal and general variety as well. He had a first name talking acquaintance with most of the Canal ghosts; leastwise, the most interesting.

When there were no genuine ghosts around, that is, when they were busy haunting (they referred to it as visiting other places), John O'Brien and the other drivers "jured" some up. New boys on the path got the full treatment. A favorite haunt for such activities was the swamp near Rome. Whenever they tied up there for the night, the old hands made for the marsh and the new boy or boys tagged along.

They gathered swamp wood, piled it, set it afire, sat circled about it and started telling ghost stories. The long orange fingers of the fire painted strange figures, gave form and substance to dancing shadows and touched gnarled trees with life and movement (to be sure, of a ghost-like quality). As the fire grew tired, content just to glow, the shadows began to hide behind the trees, to soften and melt back into the bushes, the trees, and the cat-o'-nine-tails. Meantime the Irish driver boys talked of their easy acquaintance with Canal ghosts—the good ghosts, of course, hinting there were bad ghosts, also, too frightening to talk about.

At the proper moment, however, John O'Brien would start ever so slowly to tell the weird and horrible story of the swamp ghost. So terrible was this creature from the bogs, John emphasized, that the sight of him would turn every hair on the head of the beholder snow white, and the scream that tore itself deep from the throat of the victim on the sight of the ghost would be the last human sound he would ever make. As the new driver boy sat stiff and white with fear, the older boys would slip away one by one. As John told the story, eerie sounds and weird movements came at precisely the right time from the dark edge of the firelight. The climax of the story would be accompanied by a moan which issued forth from the woods. With that, a white shape would float up from the swamp in full sight of the scared driver. With a Yess!!! the driver boy would run for the boat, head down, eyes shut, mouth open.

But the ghost story John O'Brien and his wife Alice liked best to tell their niece in later years was the tale of the Herkimer locktender and his wife. There was nothing lighthearted about this canal story. Seems that a locktender near Herkimer loved his wife very deeply. And well he might have, for a prettier lass would have been hard to find anyplace along the Canal from Waterford to Buffalo. As the tender "tended" business, his beautiful wife would pass the time of day in woman's talk with Canal cooks and wives. Every boat that passed through carried news along with its regular paying cargo. For in these years the Erie was the busiest trade route in America. Through it passed the wealth and resources of America—the world's young giant. On its waters, through its valleys, the old world moved into the new to build a modern nation in a wilderness. Locktenders needed no special qualifications beyond a strong back and the ability to guess right on Election Day. If they guessed wrong, they were out of a job. If they were right, they were sure of a job for about seven months or as long as their politics were in good order. Their job was fairly simple. When they saw a boat coming, they leaned their back against the gate and shoved. The tenders stayed in a shanty 10 × 10. The state provided lodging for the locktender and his family in a lock house generally in full view of the incoming boats.

The locktender's wife found fun in talking to the captains, especially the young ones. They generally looked her way when they could safely steal a glance. As the days passed, the locktender husband, sharply jealous to begin with, could no longer stand to see his wife looking at other men let alone talking to them. Unable to bear it longer, he finally made his wife a prisoner in their own house.

One night when he went to her room, he found her

packing her clothes. Convinced that she was running away with the young captain whose boat was tied up just below the lock, rage filled his mind and blinded his reasoning. His body seemed almost possessed. Madness streamed from his eyes. He picked up the iron poker from the floor and brought it down on her head, blow after blow. Caught in the grip of compulsion and terror, he dragged the smashed body of his wife to the lock wall, attached some stones and dumped her into the lock. Slowly the madness left him. He felt drained. He watched the body sink below the surface. A semblance of reason returned. For a moment he thought he saw the body move by itself toward the edge of the wall under the water. But no, the light was fading and his mind was playing tricks on him. In panic, he stumbled back from the lock and ran for the door of his house. Quickly, awkwardly, he tried to sop up the pool of blood, but it had already stained deep into the soft wood. Blood had splattered about the room and on his clothes. Finger lines of blood were streaked down his front where his wife, in desperation, had grabbed at him to ward off the blows. He looked about crazily, then dashed for the door. He ran right into the arms of several men who had heard the screams of the murdered woman. The sight of the blood, the wrecked room, his disheveled appearance, and the telltale poker with a blood matted clot of hair stuck to the end told a very convincing story. A blood trail led to the edge of the lock.

"Go get the constable," said one of the men. "We'll start walking him down toward the village."

"Wait 'til morning, we'll drag for the body when it's light."

They marched the locktender off to jail, and in due time justice had its way. But, strangely, the body was never found.

The day following the murder, a new man took over the lock duties. All day long he listened to stories about the murder. That night he felt considerably uneasy about going to bed in a murder room still smelling of fresh blood. Nevertheless, he slept soundly. The next night, knowing they had not found the body, he found himself more upset. That night his sleep was not undisturbed. He dreamt that the murdered woman had come for dry clothes and had laid down in the bed to rest. He awoke in a cold sweat. He sat up bolt straight. When he knew it was only a dream, he sank back into the bed weak but relaxed. Then by habit, he stretched out his arms and yawned. At the same time, his arm fell naturally over on to the pillow next to him. It felt wet. He stiffened. He turned quickly. It was wet. And there was the shape of a head on the pillow.

Panic seized him. Then slowly, his reason began to take over again. Perhaps, he thought, he had rolled over on the pillow during the night. Feeling better, he swung his feet out over the edge of the bed and again, by habit, scratched himself and rubbed his face. His face felt funny. He looked at his hands as he took them down from his face. Long strands of wet hair hung from his fingers. With a yell, he ran from the house. When he had gushed out his story, the men around the Canal only laughed at him. Most canawlers felt locktenders were a bit tetched anyway. Perhaps it all had been his imagination. With their laughs ringing in his ears, he went back to his work. That night, he placed a wood brace across the door, made sure the windows were secure, took several shots of whiskey, went to bed and eventually to sleep. Again, he had the same terrifying dream. It woke him. He was almost too afraid to feel the pillow beside him or to touch his face. Slowly, paralyzed with panic, he inched his hand over to the pillow. It was wet. He scraped at his face, long hairs clung to his cheek. The last the boatmen saw of the locktender he was running west along the Canal.

In a few days a new man took over the job. He, too, knew the story of the murder and the ghost. His mind preyed on the story. The next morning he came screaming out of the house saying he had seen the ghost of the lock. A captain grabbed him, shook the fear out of him and sat him down. But all he would do was blubber out the same story, the dream, the wet spot on the pillow and the long hairs on his face. If they wanted him to stay on the job they would have to build him a new house. Finally, to humor him and to avoid the difficulty of getting a replacement, they built a new locktender house. Never again did the ghost visit the house.

. . . "How can people believe in ghosts, Uncle John?" little Shirley would ask at the end of the story.

"Well, child," John O'Brien would say to her, "perhaps you can't, but when a'body spends a lifetime on or near the water, in the wheel house, standing on the bow, on the towpath or on a lock wall, listening to the rhythm of the water, peering into the dark, seeing pin points of light streaking out of the black marking channels and boats that can't be seen, feeling loneliness sink deep into his bones, then it's not hard to believe in other things you can't see. Especially," he would add with an Irish grin, "if you have the power."

NEVER HERO HAD A NOBLER PYRE

But where is he that helmsman bold?
The captain saw him reel,
His nerveless hands released their task
He sank beside the wheel
The wave received his lifeless corpse
Blackened with smoke and fire,
God rest him! Never hero had
A nobler funeral pyre.

JOHN MAYNARD, LAKE ERIE HERO

A little after eight o'clock the evening of August 9, 1841, the steamer *Erie*, four hours out of Buffalo and eight miles off shore about opposite Silver Creek, pushed ahead through the night toward Dunkirk in a slightly rough sea that had started to abate with a falling wind. The ship's records listed 300 people aboard. Many were Dutch emigrants. With supper over some of the passengers walked along the promenade deck. Off duty crew members relaxed in their quarters. The Captain had the *Erie* on time and on course. He was pleased. At that moment everything seemed shipshape.

Then suddenly, without warning, the boat was afire. There seemed no beginning, no spreading. Just all at once everything was burning. In moments, there was almost no escape. In the hours that followed 250 people died horribly, some of them nobly, and one, according to the Captain's testimony, very heroically. His name was Luther Fuller. He was the helmsman. What he did that tragic night marked him for lasting fame. In time and in the telling on decks, in taverns, and around the firesides, Fuller became John Maynard of the *Ocean Queen.*

> A sailor, whose heroic soul
> That hour should yet reveal,
> By name John Maynard, eastern born,
> Stood calmly at the wheel.
> "Head her southeast!" the captain shouts
> Above the smothered roar—
> "Head her south-east without delay!
> Make for the nearest shore!"

Folk heroes come in assorted shapes, sizes, places, and deeds. By their very nature they come from the imagination of people. Stories and songs of their incredible acts have brightened the loneliness of the Wisconsin woods, the river water of the Ohio and Mississippi Rivers, the rolling countryside of America's midwest, and the frontier trails of the far west. Each section claimed its favorite: the woodsman, Paul Bunyan; the keelman, Mike Fink. These are the superman variety. The rural areas preferred the milder Johnny Appleseed. The West exaggerated real characters, like Bowie, Boone, and Crockett, into frontier heroes. Since the stories about them deal with elemental vices and virtues, they are readily understood and easily loved. Most of the stories have their foundation in truth, but in the telling and retelling, writing and rewriting, the original facts are often embellished beyond recognition.

Here is the real story of John Maynard, Lake Erie hero.

It could have been just an ordinary day—that is, of course, if any day could be ordinary on the Buffalo waterfront during the 1840's. In those days most of Europe seemed to be pouring through the Erie Canal and into the emigrant steamers headed west from Buffalo for the wild frontier beyond. Several of the vessels closely nuzzled together in the Buffalo harbor had a head of steam ready for the trip up the Lakes. Into their holds, dock wholloppers rolled household goods, hardware, dry-goods, and package freight. The loaders bawled out orders to hurry it up. Passengers, scurrying in and around the high piled freight, crowded onto the gangplank. At the moment—the moment being four o'clock—most of the raucous confusion centered around the steamboat *Erie* which was about ready to leave.

Boat runners went about their business with their customary gusto; pulling, pushing, punching, persuading. Over a hundred Dutch emigrants walked down Commercial Street toward the *Erie*. Dressed in the traditional garb of their country, they made a colorful and picturesque parade as they boarded the vessel for what they hoped would be their promised land. Each clutched a carpet bag as if his life depended on it. In a sense it did. Most of them were carrying their life's earnings in specie in their bag as a grubstake in the new land. With wide-eyed wonder they jabbered among themselves. Occasionally an expletive Mein Gott, Be Jabbers, Gott in Himmel, would crackle out above the normal harbor noises. Close behind the emigrants six painters followed with their paint pots, brushes, and turpentine. They were employees of W. G. Miller's steamboat painting company of Buffalo, on their way to Erie, Pennsylvania, to repaint and decorate the steamer *James*

Madison. Standing head above the crowd just to the side of the painters was a clean shaven youth of 17 years, dressed in the uniform of a United States Military Academy Cadet. He seemed to be trying hard to look older than he actually was.

From the railing of the boat stood a group of ladies, dressed in the latest fashions, waving and calling to the people below. Some of them scattered coins to the Canal Street urchins who were tapping out dance rhythms on the dock boards. The band gaily decked in brightly colored uniforms played some of the lively tunes of the day. Standing apart from this group of ladies was Maria Jones. Her dress and manner told a story also. Her lineage was strictly Canal Street. To the initiated, that meant only one thing. Having served her apprenticeship there she was now on her way west to open her own establishment at a western Lake port.

The 300 passengers and crew represented a cross section of society. Rich and poor, moral and immoral, banker and laborer, theist and atheist. All coming from different parts of the world, all bound for different parts of the world, all filled with hopes and plans for the future. Now for a short time they would all be riding the same boat, going in the same direction, and sharing similar experiences.

Aboard the ship, meanwhile, the crew busied themselves with their respective duties. The chief and second mate checked the freight as it was stowed in the hold. In the engine room, fires were being stoked. At the tiller stood Luther Fuller. Carefully he checked the wheel and rudder. Few men had a steadier hand on the wheel than Fuller. About 28 years old, he almost seemed to have been bred to the water. The Captain had great faith in him. Outside the wheelhouse stood Captain T. J. Titus surveying and supervising the work below. Captain Titus was about 33 years old. For most of his life, he had been associated with shipping on the Great Lakes. Starting out as an able bodied seaman at sixteen, he soon worked his way up to a vessel command; first on the schooners, *United States* and *Aurora*, and then on the steamboats, *Ohio* and *Sandusky*. Since the *Erie* was first built and launched at Erie, Pennsylvania, he had been its master. This was her fourth season. Titus loved his ship. She was a magnificent vessel of over 500 tons with a very strong draft—the equal of any on the Lakes.

When everything seemed in order, Titus picked up his trumpet and shouted to the hands to cast off. The whole boat shuddered as the steam breathed life into the hull. Slowly the paddle wheels began to turn. They churned up the water. Luther Fuller headed her bow for the open lake. By his side stood Andy Blila, call boy, watching his every move. Some day he hoped to be a wheelsman like Fuller. Right now no job in the whole world seemed so important, and to Andy no one did it so well as Fuller.

When the boat was safely away from the dock, Captain Titus entered his cabin and took out his log. Under the day and date of Monday, August 9, 1841, he noted that the *Erie* had left port at 4:10 headed for Dunkirk. He also noted that a fresh wind from the south and west had roughed up the lake. After completing his entry, Titus returned to the deck. The ship had already passed the light which marked the entrance to the harbor. Passengers, however, were still lingering on the promenade deck; some were still hanging over the rails waving to the people on the dock. The faint strains of the band rose above the low rumble of the engines.

Titus liked a happy ship. He was very proud of the *Erie*. Everything seemed to shine brightly. The metal sparkled. The wood bore the high polish of new varnish. In fact, the boat had just recently been repainted inside and out. It had the pleasant smell of newness. As Titus looked about at the passengers, everyone seemed in a gay mood. Already many had begun to get acquainted. In the ladies' cabin there was talk of the latest fashions. The painters sitting fore told each other the latest bawdy jokes, roared with laughter, and speculated on what women would be available in Erie. The cadet, standing in the bow, looking forward toward Cleveland, was thinking how fine it would be to be home for a while. The Captain walked along the rail to the stern of the ship, passed the time of day with Fuller, and watched Buffalo fade out in the distance. Another voyage seemed safely under way. Fuller had managed to squeeze the *Erie* out of the crowded harbor without scratching a paddle wheel fender. It promised to be just another ordinary trip.

After Titus had satisfied himself that everything was in correct order, he returned to his cabin to prepare for dinner, usually served at five-thirty. Dinner the first night out often set the tone for the entire trip. He wanted to make sure the first meal out was happy and congenial. In the wheelhouse, Luther Fuller continued to hold a true course west by southwest as ordered. Below in the hold, the engineers fired for full speed ahead. One of the firemen on an inspection detail spotted several demijohns of turpentine atop a ledge which covered the boilers. Realizing the danger, he quickly removed them to a safer spot on the promenade deck. In the meantime, however, one of the painters returned and noticing that someone had moved their bottles of turpentine picked them up and put them back where they had been placed originally. He was, of course, unaware of the danger.

With supper over, the guests walked leisurely along the promenade deck. Occasionally lights could be seen on the south shore. Straight ahead was inky blackness. Captain Titus himself strolled along the deck and stopped not far from the pilot's house. It was now a little after eight o'clock. The Captain had been pleased with the dinner. He calculated that his ship was just about opposite Silver Creek, about eight miles from shore. While the wind had begun to subside slightly, the sea was still rough.

Then suddenly, there was a sound like an exploding bottle. It was audible only to those in the immediate vicinity of the demijohns. A puff of smoke like a cloud of coal dust followed the sound. Those who heard sucked in their breath in terror. Before anyone could say anything, a red, lurid flame reached out firing everything about it. In those few awful moments the whole boat heard the most feared word aboard ship, "Fire."

Captain Titus standing nearby saw the fire coming out of the escape pipe before he heard the yell. Skylights started cracking from the intense heat. The space between the decks was already filled with a dense red flame. Smoke poured out of the hold. Titus, acting almost instinctively, quickly turned to the bow of the ship and said to the wheelsman, "Fuller, put the wheel hard to the starboard, remain at your post, and keep the boat headed for the shore." Panic had already seized the passengers. By now the entire hold was afire. The new paint and varnish fed the flames. Desperate men pulled up boards from the deck and threw them into the water. They then jumped into the water hoping to grab hold of the board for support. In their frenzy few were able to catch hold when they came to the surface. From the cabins came the screams of those trapped behind doors. A sheet of flame blocked any hope of getting to the cabins from the outside. The sickening sweet smell of burning flesh mingled with the smell of freshly painted wood. Out on the water the screams of the drowning pierced the darkness. Curses were mixed with prayers. Most seemed to prefer drowning to burning. That seemed to be the tragic choice opened to them.

Still seeing what he could do, Titus tried to get the engineer to stop the engines in the hope that that would slacken speed and would lessen the fanning of the flames.

The intense heat made it impossible to unhook the gear. He yelled to Fuller to continue to hold fast to his course. Already flames had spread to the wheelhouse.

When Titus attempted to get to the ladies' cabin, the falling beams and flames drove him back. Inside were the life preservers which now would save no lives. He then ran forward to help with the launching of a lifeboat. No sooner did they manage to get it in the water than twenty people swamped it. Those tossed into the water struggled to stay afloat. Their arms flayed desperately at the air and water. Fear froze their faces. One by one they would grow quiet and slip beneath the water. Once again the spot would grow calm.

From the promenade deck, attempts were being made to lower the last boat. As hands hoisted it over the side, about twenty people appeared from nowhere. As soon as the boat hit the water, they were over the sides. Like the others, the boat tipped over. Within twenty minutes they were all drowned. Four men who had been swimming about grabbed hold of the keel. Titus looked about the deck. He could see no one. The boat was still headed for shore. Apparently Fuller was still at his post but it was so completely cut off by flames and smoke that it was impossible to see. When there seemed to be nothing more he could do, Titus jumped into the water. With an assist from a Negro swimming near the overturned boat, the Captain was able to grab a part of the keel.

All about him he could hear the screams of those who were drowning. He looked at the boat. It was still heading for shore. All the upper works had burned away. The hull was a dull red flame. It painted pictures of red devils dancing on the black waters. As the wind whipped the flames, it sounded to Titus like the roar of a hurricane. At the stern of the vessel, several people tried to climb down the tiller chains to the rudder. The chain was almost red hot. As they grabbed hold, the heat burned their hands.

Then, with a scream of terror, they would fall into the water. The flesh from their hands hung in shreds from the chain links. Titus noticed one man who seemed, despite the pain, to be making it down. Squinting his eyes to get better distance, Captain Titus noticed that it was the young cadet. Hand over hand he lowered himself down the chain. The pain must have been almost unbearable. Finally he made it to the rudder. He straddled the rudder and dipped his hands, burned raw by the hot chain, into water to relieve the pain. By soaking his coat in the water and wetting the area in front of him he was able to fight back the flames. He seemed older now than his 17 years.

By now it was harder to distinguish anything on the boat. Titus noticed several clinging by their fingertips to the deck edge. Afraid to drop and yet, as the flames ate closer, finding it impossible to continue to hang on. One by one the flames cut them down. The most tragic scenes of all were those of parents trying desperately and frantically to save their children. The end was always the same. It would be but a matter of moments when all would go down. Near the bulkhead the Captain watched in horrified fascination a person surrounded by fire, holding a piece of cloth in his hand. He appeared to be bathing his face to relieve the pain. All the while he was screaming for help. Then the flames hid him from view.

After two hours in the water, Titus noticed a two-stacked boat racing toward them. When it was over only fifty people were rescued. Two hundred and fifty people lost their lives. Maria Jones would never open her house. The ladies would never again bother about fashions. The girls in Erie would have to forego the pleasures of the six painters who had turned a gay boat into a funeral pyre. The immigrants would never reach the prairie land of the West.

What of the wheelsman whom Titus told to hold his course until they reached the shore? In the inquest following the tragedy, Captain Titus paid a hero's tribute to Luther Fuller, the wheelsman. "He remained at the wheel and never left it until he was burned to death." And then Titus added, "He was always a resolute man."

It could have been just another day and just another trip and Fuller could have remained just another sailor.

But this is the stuff folk heroes are made of. Among canawlers and sailors, Fuller's fame spread. In many a waterfront saloon and on the deck of many a laker his story was told over and over again. He became the symbol of the courage and strength of all Lake Erie sailors.

By 1845 his story was common property. An English traveller and writer on tour through the Lakes apparently heard the story and wrote it down. In September of that year it appeared in the Buffalo *Commercial Advertiser* and the following month in the *Western Literary Messenger* under the title "Helmsman of Lake Erie." One authority believes the author was Charles Dickens who toured the lakes in 1845.

Several alterations were made and much embellishment added to the original story. The writer rechristened the *Erie* the *Jersey* and anglicized Lake terminology. He aged Fuller considerably, renamed him John Maynard, and endowed him with all the virtues.

Old John Maynard was at the wheel—a bluff, weather-beaten sailor, tanned by many a wintry tempest. He had truly learnt to be contented with his situation: none could ever say that they ever heard him repine at his hard labor and scanty pay. He had, in the worst times, a cheerful word and a kind look for those with whom he was thrown—cast, often enough, into bad company, he tried, at least, and generally succeeded to say something for its good. He was known, from one end of the Lake Erie to the other, by the name of honest John Maynard and the secret of his honesty to his neighbors was—his love of God.

Conversation between the captain and his crew was added for dramatic emphasis.

"Dick Fletcher, what's all that smoke I see coming out from the hold?"

"It's from the engine room, sir, I guess," said the man.

"Down with you, then, and let me know."

The sailor began descending the ladder by which you go to the hold; but scarcely had he disappeared beneath the deck, when up he came again with much greater speed.

"The hold's on fire, sir," he said to the captain, who by this time was standing close to him.

The captain rushed down, and found the account too true. Some sparks had fallen on a bundle of tow; no one had seen the accident, and now not only much of the luggage, but the sides of the vessel were in smouldering flame.

All hands, passengers as well as sailors, were called together; and two lines being made, one on each side of the hold, buckets of water were passed and repassed; they were filled from the lake, they flew along a line of ready hands, were dashed hissing on the burning mass, and then passed on the other side to be refilled.

For some minutes it seemed as if the flames were subdued.

In the meantime, the women on board were clustering round John Maynard, the only man unemployed who was capable of answering their questions.

"How far is it to land?" "How long shall we be getting in?" The helmsman answered as well as he could. There was no boat: it had been left at Buffalo to be mended; they might be seven miles from shore; they would probably be in forty minutes; he could not tell how far the fire had reached. "And to speak the truth," he added, "we are all in great danger, and I think if there was a little less talking, and a little more praying, it would be better for us, and none the worse for the boat."

"How's her head?" shouted the captain.

"West-sou'west, sir" answered Maynard.

"Keep her south by west," cried the captain—

"We must go on shore any where."

It happened that a draft of wind drove back the flames, which soon began to blaze up more furiously against the saloon; and the partition betwixt it and the hold was soon on fire. Then long wreaths of smoke began to find way through the skylight, and the captain seeing this, ordered all the women forward, the engineer put on his utmost steam, the American flag was run up, and reversed, in token of distress; water was flung over the sails to make them hold the wind. And still John Maynard stood by the wheel, tho' now he was cut off, by a sheet of smoke and flames, from the ship's crew.

Greater and greater grew the heat, the engineers filed from the engine room, the passengers were clustering round the vessel's bow, the sailors were sawing planks on which to lash the women, the boldest were throwing off their coats and waistcoats, and preparing for one long struggle for life. And still the coast grew plainer and plainer; the paddles, as yet worked well; they could not be more than a mile from the shore; and boats were even now starting to their assistance.

"John Maynard!" cried the captain.

"Aye, aye, sir!" said John.

"Can you hold on five minutes longer?"

And he did try; the flames came nearer and nearer; a sheet of smoke would sometimes almost suffocate him; and his hair was singed—his blood seemed on fire with the great heat. Crouching as far back as he could, he held the wheel firmly with his left hand, till the flesh shrivelled, and the muscles cracked in the flame; and then he stretched for his right, and bore the agony without a scream or a groan. It was enough for him that he heard the cheer of the sailors to the approaching boats; the cry of the captain, "The women first, and then every man for himself, and God for us all."

And they were the last sounds that he heard. How he perished was not known; whether, dizzied by the smoke, he lost his footing in endeavoring to come forward, and fell overboard, or whether he was suffocated by the dense smoke, his comrades could not tell—At the moment the vessel struck, the boats were at her side; passengers, sailors and captain leaped into them, or swam for their lives; all, save he to whom they owed everything, escaped.

He had died the death of a Christian hero—I had almost said of a martyr; his spirit was commended into his Father's hands, and his body sleeps in peace by the green side of Lake Erie.

Probably more than anything else, this account gave John Maynard to the world. In 1875 the story was turned into poetry. Authorship has been attributed to Horatio Alger, Jr., who made his fortune as a writer of dime novels, and to Kate Weaver. The *Erie* in this work receives its third and final name, the *Ocean Queen*.

'Twas on Lake Erie's broad expanse
One bright midsummer day,
The gallant steamer Ocean Queen
Swept proudly on her way.
Bright faces clustered on the deck,
Or, leaning o'er the side,
Watched carelessly the feathery foam
That flecked the rippling tide.

Ah, who beneath that cloudless sky,
That smiling bends serene,
Could dream that danger awful vast,
Impended o'er the scene,—
Could dream that ere an hour had sped
That frame of sturdy oak
Would sink beneath the lake's blue
Blackened with fire and smoke?

A seaman sought the captain's side,
A moment whispered low;
The captain's swarthy face grew pale;
He hurried down below.
Alas, too late! Though quick, and sharp,
And clear his orders came,
No human efforts could avail
To quench th' insidious flame.

The bad news quickly reached the deck,
It sped from lip to lip,
And ghastly faces everywhere
Looked from the doomed ship.
"Is there no hope—no chance of life?"
A hundred lips implore,
"But one," the captain made reply,—
"To run the ship on shore."

A sailor, whose heroic soul
That hour should yet reveal,
By name John Maynard, eastern born,
Stood calmly at the wheel.
"Head her southeast!" the captain shouts,
Above the smothered roar—
"Head her south-east without delay!
Make for the nearest shore!"

No terror pales the helmsman's cheek,
Or clouds his dauntless eye,
As, in a sailor's measured tone,
His voice responds, "Ay! Ay!"

Three hundred souls, the steamer's freight,
Crowd forward wild with fear.
While at the stern the dreaded flames
Above the deck appear.
He grasped the wheel, and steadfastly
He steered the ship to land.

"John Maynard, can you still hold out?"
He heard the captain cry;
A voice from out the stifling smoke
Faintly responds, "Ay! Ay!"

But half a mile! a hundred hands
Stretch eagerly to shore,
But half a mile! That distance sped
Peril shall all be o'er.
But half a mile! Yet stay, the flames
No longer slowly creep,
But gather round that helmsman bold,
With fierce impetuous sweep.

"John Maynard!" with an anxious voice
That captain cries once more,
"Stand by the wheel five minutes yet,
And we shall reach the shore."
Through flame and smoke that dauntless heart
Responded firmly still,
Unawed, though face to face with death,
"With God's good help I will!"

That flames approach with giant strides,
They scorch his hand and brow;
One arm disabled, seeks his side,
Ah! he is conquered now!
But no his teeth are firmly set,
He crushes down his pain,
His knee upon the stanchion pressed,
He guides the ship again.

One moment yet! one moment yet!
Brave heart, thy task is o'er.
The pebbles grate beneath the keel,
The steamer touches shore.
Three hundred grateful voices rise
In praise to God that he

Hath saved them from the fearful fire,
And from the engulphing sea.

But where is he, that helmsman bold?
The captain saw him reel,
His nerveless hands released their task
He sank beside the wheel.
The wave received his lifeless corpse,
Blackened with smoke and fire.
God rest him! Never hero had
A nobler funeral pyre!

In 1901, John Gough, temperance leader, turned the poem into a prose oration entitled "The Pilot," and used it as a part of his vast repertoire on cross country tours. It had real punch. It eventually appeared in many school elocution books. School children memorized it. It soon reached overseas. Theodore Fontane, German poet, translated the story and poem into German. Eventually it was set to music.

Some in the United States think John Hay, Lincoln's secretary, had this story in mind when he wrote "Jim Bludso." Leastwise the Mississippi story bears a striking resemblance to the Maynard story.

The fire bust out as she clared the bar,
And burnt a hole in the night,
And quick as a flash she turned, and made
For that willer-bank on the right.
There was runnin' and cursin', but Jim yelled out,
Over all the infernal roar,
"I'll hold her nozzle agin the bank,
Till the last galoot's ashore."

Through the hot, black breath of the burnin' boat
Jim Bludso's voice was heard,

And they all had trust in his cussedness,
And knowed he would keep his word.
And, sure's you're born, they all got off
Afore the smokestacks fell,—
And Bludso's ghost went up alone
In the smoke of the Prairie Belle.

John Maynard, or Luther Fuller, might have rested in his fame if it had not been for a revelation made in 1912. Over the years, all the writers who wrote their accounts from the original stories in the newspapers or from other accounts which had themelves been based on the testimony of Captain Titus, assumed that Luther Fuller or John Maynard, as they called him, went down with his ship. This was one of the few points upon which all agreed.

On November 22, 1900, a man died in the Erie County Hospital, Erie, Pennsylvania. His name was James Rafferty. He was a common drunkard, a convicted counterfeiter and a pauper. Little notice would have been paid to his passing if the secretary of the Erie Historical Society had not in 1912 revealed that Rafferty was actually Luther Fuller, the John Maynard of Lake Erie fame. According to him, Fuller had stayed with the ship until all had left and then when the rudder ropes had burned and it was useless for him to stay aboard, he cut away a part of the paddle wheel fender and floated ashore. He had been badly burned.

Credence was placed immediately in the secretary's story because he had been little Andy Blila, the call boy on the *Erie* the night it burned. Fuller often came into his father's saloon, Blila claimed, to borrow a dime for a drink. So it was that the man who had been capable, at least once in his life, of rising to such great heights, died a convicted criminal and drunkard, not far from the water where he had played out his heroic deed. But whatever happened to James Rafferty, John Maynard would always remain the hero of Lake Erie.

The Empty Bottle

THE EMPTY BOTTLE

This world is a bottle,
Our life is a dram;
When the bottle is empty
It ain't worth a damn.

From Daca's New Door Bookstore
Washington Square, New York City

INDEX